NINETEENTH- AND TWENTIETH-CENTURY
# EUROPEAN DRAWINGS AND SCULPTURE
## FROM THE SCHLOSSBERG COLLECTION

INTRODUCTORY ESSAY BY
## ERIC M. ZAFRAN
ASSOCIATE CURATOR OF EUROPEAN PAINTING
MUSEUM OF FINE ARTS, BOSTON

EXHIBITION ORGANIZED BY
## PAULA MARLAIS HANCOCK
ADJUNCT CURATOR
HIGH MUSEUM OF ART

JUNE 11-SEPTEMBER 11, 1994

HIGH MUSEUM OF ART
ATLANTA, GEORGIA

Copyright 1994 High Museum of Art
All rights reserved
Published by the High Museum of Art,
Atlanta, Georgia

Edited by Kelly Morris
Designed by Jim Zambounis, Atlanta
Type set by Katherine Gunn
Printed by The Stinehour Press,
Lunenburg, Vermont

Library of Congress No. 94-076254
ISBN 0-939802-76-7

Cover: Eugène Delacroix, *Studies after
Michelangelo* (no. 18).

# CONTENTS

# ACKNOWLEDGEMENTS

Having first encountered the enthusiastic collector Michael Schlossberg and his already substantial collection of drawings in 1979 when I was curator of European art at the High Museum, it is a distinct pleasure to have returned to Atlanta to find that this collection has grown tremendously and now embraces sculpture as well. To create a coherent exhibition, we have decided to focus here only on the European works and these are almost entirely of the nineteenth and twentieth centuries. Like any collection, this one has a distinctive flavor, which I hope can be conveyed to some extent in the introductory essay, but will be even more evident in the pleasure of viewing the works of art themselves.

In carrying out my task I wish to thank the collectors Lana and Michael Schlossberg for graciously making themselves, the collection, and their documentation available for my study. Dr. Paula Hancock, who has co-ordinated the exhibition in exemplary fashion, provided the utmost moral and intellectual support. At the High Museum I would also like to thank the director Ned Rifkin and associate director William Bodine for inviting me to participate in this project. Kelly Morris continues to be a peerless editor, and the registrarial and exhibition departments of the Museum are to be commended on attending so efficiently to all the details of the exhibition and its tour.

Eric M. Zafran

An exhibition of Michael and Lana Schlossberg's collection was first proposed in 1989 by Gudmund Vigtel, then director of the High Museum of Art. Following his retirement, the commitment to the exhibition was continued by the new director, Dr. Ned Rifkin.

During the course of shaping this exhibition, many others have provided assistance. Eric Zafran has written an eloquent essay on the Schlossbergs' European collection, perceptively evoking the works themselves and the collecting spirit that animates the collection. My colleagues at the High Museum of Art—Susan Krane, curator of modern and contemporary art, Judy Larson, curator of American art, and Ronni Baer, Frances B. Bunzl Family curator of European art—were involved at the early stages of the exhibition, and I am pleased to acknowledge their continuing interest in the project. Associate director William Bodine has helped bring the exhibition to fruition. Kelly Morris has guided the publication of the catalogue, and Jim Zambounis has provided an elegant and appropriate design. Registrar Frances Francis and associate registrar Jody Cohen have overseen the myriad details of caring for and transporting the works of art. Marjorie Harvey has planned the installation with sensitivity and imagination. Gail Harris and Joy Wasson provided essential administrative support.

Seeing cherished objects under curatorial scrutiny cannot be easy for any collector. For months, the Schlossbergs graciously allowed me access to their collection without reservation, enduring the process of selection and gathering of information with characteristic generosity and enthusiasm. At every turn they have made progress toward exhibition a pleasurable adventure. To Michael and Lana Schlossberg go first and foremost thanks for making this exhibition possible.

Paula Marlais Hancock

# FOREWORD

Museums collect art with the multiple purposes of preserving the objects, researching their historical and cultural context, and interpreting the art for a projected audience. While personal taste and sensibility inevitably enter into acquisition decisions on the institutional level, it is a distinctly different enterprise and activity than the collecting done by the individual collector. Whereas the museum serves a somewhat anonymous public —be it a rarified and refined small public or a vast one—the individual collector is untethered by the responsibilities of accounting for his or her curatorial orientation.

More often than not, great museum collections are the result of private connoisseurship and philanthropy which, at some point or another, are transferred to the institution. It is the exceptional museum that has sufficient funds to apply to the building of a collection. In this regard, the collaboration of individual collector and institution is an especially important partnership.

Atlanta has not been known nationally as a city of great or extensive private art collections. There may well be reasons for this, although I suspect that part of this is that few exhibitions like the one being presented here have featured individuals' collections that testify to the contrary. Thus it is with great delight and considerable pleasure that we present *Nineteenth- and Twentieth-Century European Drawings and Sculpture from the Schlossberg Collection* at the High Museum of Art. The exhibition demonstrates the intelligence, sensitivity, and commitment of a couple who have quietly, but insistently, put together an important collection of fine quality nineteenth- and twentieth-century European drawings and sculptures.

Equally important is that Michael and Lana Schlossberg have permitted this museum to select a portion of their collection as a model and, hopefully, inspiration to other aspiring collectors. It is critical to the welfare of cultural life here—

and elsewhere—that collecting art be seen as and understood as both a feasible and an entirely engaging and rewarding activity. The beauty of the works of art is obvious to anyone who sees them. But the realization of any fine collection, one that reflects a personal passion as well as an informed and expert pursuit, is always greater than the sum of its parts. It reflects a spirit of adventure, a sense of duty, and a mission of discovery, both about the art and about oneself.

This project would not have been realized had it not been for the dedication of Dr. Paula Hancock, adjunct curator at the High. Dr. Hancock's diligence, fastidious attention to detail, sensitivity to the material, and thoughtful selection of the individual works have made this a very special exhibition indeed. We are also very grateful for the work of Dr. Eric Zafran, associate curator of European art at the Museum of Fine Arts in Boston (and former curator of European art here at the High), for his insightful essay, which illuminates our understanding of the art. I also wish to thank William B. Bodine, Jr., associate director for museum programs, for his work coordinating aspects of this project.

Of course, without the rigors of collecting and the willingness to share the fruits on the part of Michael and Lana Schlossberg, there would be no exhibition. Atlanta is fortunate to have individuals who have demonstrated such a profound commitment to collecting. I salute and thank the Schlossbergs for their generosity of spirit and for their accomplishments in bringing together these remarkable objects.

Ned Rifkin, Director

# PREFACE

I have been asked to write something about this collection of sculptures and drawings, and this is a difficult request, since they are only part of a much greater whole, and one does not like to slight any of one's beloved children. It is fair to say I have been a compulsive collector all my life, beginning with stamps, coins, baseball cards, and comics when I was younger. I still have a large collection of cartoon art and also have had African and Haitian art, and continue to pursue American works, including Georgia folk art.

My initiation into the world of European drawings, however, happened almost by chance. When living in New York City in the early 1960s during my medical residency, I went to a small auction in Queens to look at some prints by Rouault and Chagall. There I bought for only forty dollars a small drawing by Theo van Rysselberghe, an artist I actually knew of from my previous reading. It was a real thrill for me to possess a unique and original art work and I have never entirely gotten over that feeling. My interest in the late nineteenth century was further sparked when, during military service at Fort Sam Houston in Texas in 1967, I found by chance a battered copy of John Rewald's *History of Post-Impressionism*. This book became my escape from the drudgery of army life. Rewald's anecdotal approach brought the personalities of the artists to life, and planted the seed for my interest in this area that has become the core of the European collection.

The American school continued to occupy me and I was able to acquire drawings by such important artists as Edward Hopper and Ben Shahn. Gradually, by studying the auction sales and visiting the dealers in New York, I began adding more Europeans; often they came in waves, and I recall that two of the Gauguins were bought on one occasion. I was always especially pleased to obtain works that had come from earlier notable collectors such as Benjamin Sonnenberg, Ian Woodner, Maurice Bloch, the Avnets, and others.

The enthusiastic encouragement I received from the High Museum's first curators, Peter Morrin and Eric Zafran, to both refine and continue the collection of drawings was of great importance. Therefore, I am particularly delighted that the latter—now at the Museum of Fine Arts in Boston—has been able to turn his enlightened eye and scholarly mind to the much expanded collection. Although I had already acquired bronzes by the contemporary American artist Leonard Baskin and had a few unusual pieces, such as the Raffaëlli bust, the impetus to seriously pursue European sculpture to complement the drawings came primarily from the dealers David and Constance Yates, whom I first met in the late 1970s. We began with David d'Angers, who is now well represented by some excellent casts, and have progressed to probably my most significant recent purchase, the Rodin plaster in this exhibition.

I want to thank the director, trustees, and staff of the High Museum for inviting me to present this selection of works to the public in Atlanta and elsewhere. I hope they will derive as much enjoyment from seeing it as my wife Lana and I have had in assembling it.

Michael Schlossberg

# THE SCHLOSSBERG COLLECTION OF EUROPEAN DRAWINGS AND SCULPTURE

### AN APPRECIATION BY
### ERIC M. ZAFRAN

This exhibition of more than one hundred drawings and sculptures is primarily French and mostly of the nineteenth and twentieth centuries. The selection presented here reflects one but by no means the sole area of concentration for the collectors, Michael and Lana Schlossberg. The collection, while not intended to be encyclopedic in content, has nevertheless grown to include works from most of the significant movements of this period and by many of the most famous artists. Yet it is not merely a collection of names, but rather an assemblage rich in cross references to the creative individuals who flourished during this era and marked by distinctive themes that we shall explore.

## NINETEENTH-CENTURY DRAWINGS

Most of the nineteenth-century drawings are studies of the human figure. This interest in the human form (to be expected perhaps from a medical doctor) is conjoined with a concern for fine draughtsmanship. There is evidenced in this collection a definite predilection for works which display the tradition of academic training that made it possible for an artist to correctly delineate—in pen and ink, red or black chalk, or graphite and wash—the forms of the human body before committing them to canvas.

The mastery of drawing from a model in preparation for a larger composition is revealed in one of the earliest sheets in the exhibition, a red chalk drawing of an old woman (no. 37, illustrated, p. 23) by the late eighteenth-century master Jean-Baptiste Greuze. The work reveals his powerful, even aggressive, rendering of the human form. The subject is an angular character type Greuze frequently employed, and in this case the drawing is a preparatory study for a figure in one of his finest oil paintings, *The Paralytic* of 1760 (Hermitage Museum, St. Petersburg).[1] Greuze, who achieved fame for this kind of large-scale, mor-

alizing genre painting, had been something of a child prodigy as a draughtsman. But at the Académie royale, like all the aspiring artists of his time, he had to conform to the strict system of learning to draw by copying casts, followed by intensive study of the live model. When this had been mastered, the artist possessed the facility to make the preparatory studies for whatever compositions his imagination could conceive. This system was carried on into the nineteenth century, despite the Revolution, and continued to be the approach adopted by traditional artists through the end of the century.

Jacques-Louis David was the prince of artistic affairs in Paris during the Revolution and again under Napoleon, due to his ability to create popular images of great clarity and severe beauty based on ancient prototypes. David painted several grand propagandistic subjects for the Emperor. The many figures in these paintings involved tremendous amounts of preliminary study, none more so than the vast canvas depicting Napoleon's coronation in Notre Dame on December 2, 1804. Traditionally known as *Le Sacre*, the painting in the Louvre is now generally referred to as *Le Couronnement de L'Empereur et de l'Imperatrice*, since its theme evolved from showing Napoleon crowning himself to the moment when he crowns the Empress Josephine before the assembled court, the pope, church dignitaries, and literary and artistic luminaries.[2] In the painting Napoleon's mother, who had not actually attended the event, was given a prominent place. As he did for each figure, David made a life study of her in her coronation finery.[3] Once this painting was completed in 1808, David commenced work on a replica, now in Versailles, that he finished during his exile at Brussels in 1822. For this he made another series of preliminary drawings, and as the drawing in the Schlossberg collection (no. 14, illustrated, p. 28) is inscribed *Par David de souvenir* (by David from memory), it may be one of this later group.[4] The subject is the poet Ponce Denis Ecouchard Lebrun (1729-1807), who was known as "Lebrun-Pindare" for his mastery of the classical modes, but who is perhaps better remembered for his political flexibility, having gone from serving the *ancien regime* to being the official poet of the Terror, and then finally becoming an enthusiastic supporter of Napoleon. Thus he was given a prime seat at the coronation, shown seated in the front row behind and to the viewer's right of the Emperor's mother. The drawing shows him wearing a visor, which is reminiscent of the wreaths often depicted on ancient poets and also serves to frame Lebrun's face with its suggestion of the ironic wit that helped earn him as many enemies as friends.

The neo-classical style perfected by David was to have wide-spread appeal, and echoes of it are found not only throughout the continent but also in England. Benjamin West's *Lion* (no. 92, illustrated, p. 23) is perhaps the most anomalous drawing in the Schlossberg collection, for it is first of all a study of an animal, a recumbent lion, and is by the only artist represented in the exhibition who was born in America. West, after an early period copying European prints in his native Philadelphia, departed for Italy in 1760 and three years later settled in London, never to return to his native land. He so successfully adopted the approved classical manner of painting that he became president of the Royal Academy and was befriended by the king, George III. It may have been in the royal menagerie that West had the opportunity to see a real lion and make this drawing on blue paper, which was then incorporated into his 1809 painting *Omnia Vincit Amor* (Metropolitan Museum of Art, New York).[5]

David, in order to carry out his vast projects, had a great many students and followers. The most talented of these, and the one who may be said to have elevated the traditional methods of draughtsmanship to their highest peak, was Jean-Auguste-Dominique Ingres. This artist, born in Montauban, was David's student from 1797 until he won the Prix de Rome in 1801. Ingres was not able to enjoy his reward, a trip to Rome, until the fall of 1806, but once in Italy he remained for eighteen years. He benefited greatly from his study of ancient art and the Renaissance masters, especially Raphael, who helped inspire the precise, linear style Ingres perfected in both his paintings and drawings. The small but exquisite drapery study (no. 45, illustrated, p. 29) in the Schlossberg collection is typical of his method of drawing with a sharply pointed graphite pencil on smooth white paper.

After his return to Paris, Ingres became in turn the master of a large atelier that eventually trained over a hundred students. They followed his careful, classical style and emulated his manner of executing portrait drawings, employing delicate, thin lines to represent the contours of the clothed body and a denser, more elaborate treatment of the head and hair, so that the sitter's face seems to jump off the sheet of paper at the viewer. Of these lesser-known but highly skilled artists, there is an excellent example by Eugène-Emmanuel Amaury-Duval (no. 2), which is a veritable tour de force in its manipulation of the graphite line to achieve texture and shading. In addition to being a talented artist, Amaury-Duval was the author of *L'Atelier d'Ingres*, a book that provided important information on the master and his best students.[6]

Another of Ingres's followers, also represented by a portrait study in the Schlossberg collection, was Hippolyte Flandrin (no. 21, illustrated, p. 28). Also from Ingres's circle are preliminary drawings for larger compositions by Henri Lehmann and Léon Bénouville. Lehmann's sensitive studies of a young boy, dated 1859 (no. 47, illustrated, p. 33), were preparatory for the figure of an angel illustrating the section *Adveniat regnum tuum* (Thy kingdom come) of a six-part paraphrase of the Pater noster (The Lord's Prayer), a long-planned but never executed large-scale decorative scheme for the interior of the Church of Sainte-Clotilde in Paris.[7] The toga-encased head of a man (no. 4) by Bénouville is most likely a study for one of many Roman figures seated in the stadium shown in his large Salon painting of 1855, *Les Martyrs conduits au supplice*.[8]

Also of this generation was the painter and illustrator Isidore Alexandre Auguste Pils. Although he received his formal training in the studio of Picot, Pils encountered Ingres as director of the French Academy in Rome when he went there as the winner of the Prix de Rome in 1838. Pils endorsed the traditional method of training young artists,[9] and is represented here by an entire sketchbook (no. 62), a telling example of the industry and talent of the artist, for almost every page bears a striking portrait, figure study, or landscape. The portrait of Alexandre Dumas fils is particularly noteworthy.

If Ingres and his school are the pinnacle of refined draughtsmanship in nineteenth-century France, Eugène Delacroix and his followers in the Romantic movement represent the opposite extreme. More concerned in his paintings with color than form, Delacroix in his drawings practiced a looser, freer, more expressive style than Ingres. His tremendous bravado imbued even the humblest pen sketch with a quivering immediacy. Despite his somewhat controversial style, Delacroix's genius was never in doubt, and throughout his career he received important official commissions. His creative struggle to fulfill these is evidenced in the continual revisions of his preliminary studies. One such project was the ceiling decoration of the Deputies' Library in the Palais Bourbon, on which he worked from 1838 to 1847. For the ceiling's oddly shaped pendentives, he conceived a series devoted to creative men of the past—philosophers, writers, and artists. His study for Michelangelo (no. 17, illustrated, p. 30) is one of several variants on this theme that Delacroix developed but ultimately did not use in the finished series.[10] Instead, the sculptor's attributes, a mallet and a marble bust, were eliminated and the subject became Socrates, thus adhering better to the general theme of the ancient world that dominates the ceiling cycle. Michelangelo, shown here with a large craggy head and powerful forearms, was one of Delacroix's heroes, and we can well understand why he originally sought to include him in this grandiose scheme.

Delacroix, however, found other ways of paying homage to the Italian master by incorporating the sculptural monumentality of Michelangelo's creations into his own paintings. Delacroix never went to Italy, but he of course knew the works by Michelangelo in the Louvre and (through prints) his other masterpieces, many of which he copied.[11] The two headless muscular torsos seen on the other Delacroix sheet in the exhibition (no. 18, illustrated, cover and p. 24) are both based on well-known Michelangelos. The upper one is after the marble allegorical figure of Dawn from the Medici tombs in San Lorenzo, Florence, and the lower, more heavily shaded figure is the famous Adam from the Sistine Chapel.

Although his drawing is unusually bold for a derivative work, Delacroix's practice of copying earlier masters was in fact a traditional and popular way for artists to absorb the lessons of their predecessors. Within the present exhibition, there are drawings ranged throughout the nineteenth century that show young artists learning by copying earlier works of art. These include Jules Elie Delaunay's delicate graphite drawing (no. 19) after a portion of Raphael's Vatican fresco of *The Fire in the Borgo*, Géricault's enlarged and colorful interpretation of an ancient engraved gem known

to him from a print (no. 33, illustrated, p. 24),[12] Degas's refined study after an antique head (no. 16), and Seurat's after a Holbein (no. 80).

Another nineteenth-century movement which owed a great deal to Delacroix was generally referred to as "Orientalism." Delacroix's journey of 1832 to Morocco produced so much radiant and memorable imagery that many other artists followed in his footsteps. Among those who went to the East and recorded in their sketches the exotic peoples of North Africa were both Bida (no. 6) and Fromentin (no. 26). Later in the century came another popular phase known as *Japonisme*, and representative of this decorative style is the fan-shaped composition by Henri Somm (no. 84) that shows a French lady in Japanese costume.

In the later part of the nineteenth century, the art world in France can be loosely divided into two camps. There was one group which continued to follow the accepted canon of careful draughtsmanship and the accurate portrayal of subject matter—whether it be myth, history, portraiture, or the now more popular anecdotal genre. These (for the most part) conservative or academic artists were the ones who had control of the annual Paris Salon, where all painters and sculptors hoped to obtain a public showing for their talent. They were opposed by a steady stream of revolutionary individuals, who in the name of realism, naturalism, or impressionism proposed a more personal, immediate style devoted to humble and transient aspects of the everyday world. Both camps are well represented in the Schlossberg collection.

If an average French person had been asked during the years 1850-1890 who was the most famous living artist, he would probably have answered "Meissonier." This Lyon-born master had made his reputation early for small-scale, minutely rendered recreations of eighteenth-century scenes and then went on to paint well-known patriotic images of the Napoleonic era. His subsequent fame derived as much from his financial success, clever self-promotion, and grandiose life style as from his art.[13] He was, nevertheless, a highly gifted self-taught technician, and his ability to portray detailed historical scenes in a miniature format is especially evident in his many book illustrations, for one of which the drawing displayed here is a preliminary study (no. 53, illustrated, p. 32).

The taste for anecdotal genre subjects popularized by Meissonier was continued by the painter Jehan Georges Vibert, who specialized in eighteenth-century subjects, endless depictions of cardinals, and also Spanish scenes.[14] It is the last category that is represented by the drawing of *The Knife Grinder* (no. 90, illustrated, p. 38), a charming souvenir of the trip Vibert, like so many French artists and writers of his era, took to the colorful land beyond the Pyrennes.

Another popular subject treated by several of the fashionable Salon artists was the sentimental representation of Italian peasants, especially young women in their colorful native costumes. Léon Bonnat's preparatory drawing (no. 7) is for one of his best known paintings of this theme, *La Pasqua Maria*, which was exhibited at the Salon of 1863, where its coy charm evoked an enthusiastic response from the influential critic Théophile Gautier.[15] Later in his career Bonnat devoted his undoubted talents to portraiture, especially of the many rich Americans who visited Paris at this time, as well as of his circle of distinguished, artistic friends, like the sculptor Auguste Nadaud (no. 8, illustrated, p. 39).

Always also to be seen at the Salons were large-scale religious pictures. Jean-Jacques Henner was one of the artists who was able to paint such traditional matter but make it fresh and suggestive through his inclusion of sensual nudes, both male and female, veiled in a hazy *sfumato*. A favorite subject of Henner was St. Irene tending the wounds of St. Sebastian. His moving conception, which in many ways recalls a traditional Pietà, was given expression in a large painting shown at the Salon of 1888 and the Exposition Universelle the following year and in a number of smaller painted and drawn versions, such as the one in black and white chalk exhibited here (no. 42, illustrated, p. 34).[16] Another painter who first made his reputation with religious and historical subjects before turning to fashionable contemporary scenes was Jacques Joseph Tissot. His first paintings were in a style heavily influenced by earlier Flemish and Italian works. This was quite evident in the three he exhibited at the Salon of 1863. For one of these, *The Departure of the Prodigal Son from Venice*, the Schlossberg collection holds the decidedly old masterish drawing of two key figures (no. 87, illustrated, p. 33).[17]

Yet another group of painters who exhibited at the Salon specialized in scenes of rural life. The struggle of the peasants to eke out a bare existence was romanticized, and picturesque representations of gnarled old farm folks were offset by those of robust country girls. The former category is treated in the present exhibition in a powerful example by one of the foremost practioneers of the rural genre, Léon Lhermitte (no. 48, p. 34), and

the latter in a drawing by Pascal Dagnan-Bouveret (no. 12). Also related to this category of earthy artists are François Bonvin and Théodule Auguste Ribot. Bonvin, inspired by the example of the eighteenth-century master Chardin, produced his own version of rustic genre, often depicting scenes from the humble life of serving people. The study of an old man (no. 9, illustrated, p. 39) is a good example of Bonvin's sympathetic art. Ribot frequently used members of his own homely family (no. 71, illustrated, p. 38) as models for his rough-hewn images of working people.

The sentimentality, grandiloquence, and polish of the works produced by artists such as Bonnat, Henner, and Vibert was challenged by the group of young artists who—after their first joint exhibition in 1874—came to be known as the Impressionists. The very term implies a good deal of what they attempted to do: to capture a spontaneous moment in time, to render the look and atmosphere of everyday settings and people. Despite what was written about them at the time, all these artists had had some formal training in drawing and, although they might not have liked to admit it, often relied on quickly rendered preliminary sketches to help capture the fleeting impressions they sought.

Although Edouard Manet was not formally a member of the exhibiting Impressionists, he served in many ways as their mentor. Primarily known for his large compositions of modern themes which shocked complacent bourgeoise mores, Manet was also a talented portraitist. With paint, pen, pastel, or graphite, he was able to rapidly capture the features of his sitters, such as his friend the the writer Henri Vigneau (no. 51, illustrated, p. 35).[18] Manet's influence on the younger artists of the Impressionist movement is given particularly vivid form in one of the most unusual drawings in the Schlossberg collection, Renoir's copy after Manet's famous painting *The Fifer* (no. 70, illustrated, p. 35). Renoir prepared this on the occasion of a Manet memorial exhibition in 1883, for publication in the January 1884 edition of the popular magazine *La Vie Moderne*, of which his brother Edmond was chief editor.[19]

Of the other major Impressionists, we have already noted the sheet by Degas (no. 16), and there is also a rare landscape study by Alfred Sisley (no. 83, illustrated, p. 37), a blur of trees and fields that is characteristic of the type of preliminary sketches made by both Monet and Sisley. This one, according to Francois Daulte, "is probably a study for one of the paintings titled *La Route de Veneux à Moret*, which Sisley painted ca. 1887-1890."[20] Among the rather contentious Impressionists, the most diplomatic and certainly the most sympathetic was Camille Pissarro. He was as devoted to the natural world as he was to his large family, which he immortalized in a marvelous drawing (no. 65, illustrated, p. 37) that shows him as a *pater familias* slumbering in an easy chair and imagining his wife hard at work and all his children as active, if not hugely successful, artists.

Exhibiting with the Impressionists in 1880 and 1881 was the Paris-born painter Jean-François Raffaëlli. While his work at this time, primarily genre scenes, resembled the Impressionists', he soon developed a more illustrative manner, depicting both the fashionable and the seamy sides of Parisian life. Raffaëlli's narrative talents made him popular in the United States, which he visited in 1895 on the occasion of an exhibition of his works in New York City.[21] He even received commissions from America, including one from *Harper's* in 1889 to illustrate an article on the well-known Paris auction gallery The Hôtel Drouot. Theodore Child's article described the section of the establishment known as the Mazas, where possessions belonging to the impoverished were sold; there was "horrible pandemonium, haunted by marine store dealers, old clothes men, low brokers and commercial scavengers of all degrees, wreckers, who gather up the flotsam and jetsam of misfortune, misconduct, satiety, sudden death, and suicide."[22] All this is well conveyed by Raffaëlli's ink and watercolor drawing (no. 67, illustrated, p. 40) that shows the shabby, distraught men and women tightly packed around a bare table.

The next generation of painters—who first learned from the Impressionists' spontaneity, but then turned to concerns with symbolic meaning and color theory—have been lumped together under the unsatisfactory term Post-Impressionists. The chief catalyst of this group was the enigmatic Paul Gauguin, and it is in his works and those of his circle that the Schlossberg collection makes perhaps its greatest contribution to our knowledge. From Gauguin's early career is a double-sided sheet from a sketch book that later was in the possession of the artist's son Pola (no. 27, illustrated, p. 43). On one side it shows a cello player and on the other a sleeping child. Richard Brettell has written to the collector:

> I think there is little doubt that the cellist is Gauguin himself and that the omission of his right hand and the cello was made for the obvious technical reasons. The drawing must relate to the Courbet self-portrait as a cellist from the Arosa collection, which was sold in February of 1878 and of which Gauguin possessed first hand knowledge and the sales catalogue. The drawing on the verso relates without question to the sleeping infant painting of 1884 now in the Josefowitz collection. The identity of that child has never been firmly established, with various views that it is Aline or Jean-René.[23]

Brettell adds that Gauguin's self-portrait as a cellist is "the link between the Courbet self-portrait and Gauguin's ambiguous [portrait of the cellist] Upaupa Schneklud painting of 1894 in the Baltimore Museum. For that reason this sheet is one of a handful of early works of art in which Gauguin probed his own identity as an artist and as a man."[24]

In search of this identity Gauguin sought out "primitive" locales, where he hoped to escape the corrupting influences of civilization and find an unspoiled realm where man and nature were in harmony. First, in 1886 he went to Pont-Aven in Brittany, where there was already an artist's colony and where he was fascinated by the dress, customs, and piety of the local people. In 1887 he set sail for Panama, which provided no sustenance to his art, and then briefly on to Martinique. But after a short creative period, he fell ill and had to return to France, where he stayed with the painter Claude Emile Schuffenecker before going back to Pont-Aven in 1888. This time he was the center of attention for the artists assembled there and remained so on succeeding stays in 1889 and 1890.

Among these younger painters was Paul Sérusier, the future father of the symbolist group which called itself the Nabis, after the Hebrew word for prophet. Sérusier, who benefitted greatly from Gauguin's ideas, left an important drawing (no. 77, illustrated, p. 44) as a record of their encounter in Brittany. This includes portrait heads of both Gauguin and the ascetic Nabi Paul Ranson, plus sketches of the local populace and their rustic houses. It was the latter subject matter which came to fascinate Sérusier as much as Gauguin, and he gave the distinctive Breton women even greater prominence in a large drawing of the 1890s (no. 78, illustrated, p. 44). Based upon the style of the headresses, Caroline Boyle-Turner has concluded that the drawing must have been done in the village of Huelgoat.[25]

Gauguin, in his quest for the ideal setting, embarked for Tahiti in April 1891 and for some time remained fascinated by the strange people and vegetation he found there. He was back in Europe, however, from August 1893 to July 1895, at which time he settled in a more remote part of Tahiti, where he often lived in great despair but produced some of his most magisterial works, filtering native concepts through his own symbolist aesthetic. To achieve his haunting images he still employed the old-fashioned method of making preliminary drawings on the fragments of paper available to him. One of the most fascinating is a sheet which on one side shows another slumbering child (no. 29, illustrated, p. 43), who is quite close to that seen on the ground at the lower right corner of Gauguin's greatest Tahitian painting, *Where do you come from? Who are we? Where are we going?* (1897, now in the Museum of Fine Arts, Boston). On the other side are diverse sketches that seem to relate to other works of this period. The two figures riding on horseback seen from the back are reminiscent of those in several paintings, especially *The White Horse* (1898, Musée d'Orsay, Paris) and *Riders on the Beach* (1902, Niarchos collection).[26] The sleek animal closest to the bottom of the Schlossberg page is nearly identical to that in the painting *Te rerioa (The Dream)* (1897, Courtauld Gallery, London), which also includes a sleeping child.[27]

This exhibition includes several drawings by artists who were part of Gauguin's circle of acquaintances in addition to those of Sérusier. Gauguin's devoted friend Schuffenecker executed the portrait study of the painter Emile Bernard (no. 76), one of the most precocious of the original Nabis, as a variant on the theme of the pensive writer that he designed for the cover of the political journal *L'Eclair*.[28] Bernard himself is represented by one of his more romantic *fête galante* subjects of the years 1889-90, when he turned to more decorative compositions (no. 5, illustrated, p. 26).[29] The same is true of the Nabi Henri-Gabriel Ibels, who in order to survive provided illustrations for posters, menus, and magazines (no. 44, illustrated, p. 36).[30]

The painters Edouard Vuillard and his brother-in-law Ker Xavier Roussel, who first met in 1888, were also members of the Nabi group in their younger days. Later they both pursued quite different styles. Vuillard devoted himself to domestic interiors captured in what John Russell has described as "a darting, elliptic, first-hand way."[31] These intimate scenes often depict his seamstress mother in the cozy apartment they shared until her death (no. 91). Roussel's forte on the other hand became large-scale decorative works with pastoral and pagan themes, but in this exhibition we see him as a portraitist, setting down the features of the reclusive Vuillard (no. 74).

In addition to these figurative studies, there are also two fine landscapes of Brittany by other colleagues of Gauguin. The first is a modified synthesist view of the countryside in muted colors by one of the founding members of the Nabis, Paul Ranson (no. 69, illustrated, p. 43).[32] The other is by the Irish painter Roderic O'Conor, who studied art in Dublin and then moved to France, attracted by the revolutionary movements on the continent. He may have made his first visit to Pont-Aven in 1887 but was definitely there in 1891-1892 and again in 1894, when he became friendly with Gauguin, even being one of the latter's party that was beaten up by sailors in Concarneau. Athough at this time O'Conor had not seen many of the canvases from Gauguin's first Tahitian period, it was clear that, as Clive Bell has written, "Gauguin's strength of character and convincing style of talk made a deep impression on the young, or youngish, Irishman. . . ."[33] The rather muscular style of simplified natural forms that O'Conor adopted after this encounter found perhaps its most powerful expression in the paintings and drawings (no. 57) he did along the rugged Brittany coast at Le Pouldu.[34]

Just as Gauguin was the lightning rod for one group of the Post-Impressionists, so Georges Seurat was for those who called themselves "divisionists." Seurat began his training in the traditional manner at the Ecole des Beaux-Arts in 1878 by attending the classes of Ingres's student Henri Lehmann, and this is evident in the stylized, Flaxman-like treatment of his early classical drawings (no. 79, illustrated, p. 41). Following this schooling Seurat in 1879-1880 had a year of military service in an infantry regiment stationed at Brest, but he continued his artistic endeavors by keeping a sketchbook. A sheet from this book (no. 81, illustrated, p. 27) reveals that he was already beginning to develop the style of reducing form to strong outlines with shading achieved by clustering strokes of the colored crayons. When he returned to Paris he perfected a system of graduated masses of color or (in his drawings) of evocative black and white tonalities.

The writer and critic Félix Fénéon, who at one time owned all the Seurat drawings in this exhibition, came to the defense of Seurat and his circle after their showing at the eighth and last Impressionist exhibition in 1886 and coined for them the term "neo-impresionists." Of this group, which formed around the charismatic but difficult Seurat, we have late, realistic examples by Maximilien Luce (no. 49) and Theo van Rysselberghe (no. 75, illustrated, p. 25). For a quintessential example of neo-impressionist draughtsmanship, one must turn to the beautiful drawing by Charles Angrand (no. 3, illustrated, p. 42), a close friend of Seurat's whose drawings were greatly admired by the other members of this group. When in 1899 Angrand exhibited at the Durand-Ruel Gallery a series of highly finished, evocative charcoal drawings on the mother-and-child theme (probably including this drawing), his colleague Paul Signac aptly described them as "poems of light."[35]

Contemporary with the Post-Impressionists were the artists identified as Symbolists, who like the poets and writers of the time, sought to transform modern life by introducing "phantoms of dreams, of hallucinations, of memories, [and] imaginary creations."[36] Symbolism was never a very organized or consistent movement, but several of the artists who were involved with it are to be found in the present exhibition. Eugène Carrière from Strasbourg went to Paris in 1869 and gradually developed a treatment of forms enveloped in mist for his many depictions of his family and others, giving the works a great sense of mystery (no. 11). Henri Martin from Toulouse, after study in Paris, travelled in Italy and there discovered the early Florentine painters, who would influence his later allegorical and religious paintings. One of these, commissioned by the French govenment in 1892 and entitled *L'Inspiration*, shows an apparition of a nude woman appearing to a painter in a church interior.[37] Martin used his friend the sculptor Alexandre Charpentier as his model for the bearded painter, and made a wonderful charcoal study of him (no. 52). The Algerian-born Armand Point was also inspired by earlier Italian art, though his style was more delicate than Martin's. In 1896 Point founded an artist-workers community at Marlotte to produce bronzes and decorative arts. His interest in jewelery is evident in the Leonardesque head study (no. 66, illustrated, p. 25), which also reveals how close his manner is to that of the English Pre-Raphaelites.[38]

As might be expected of a collector who had an early interest in cartoon art, there is in this collection and exhibition a strong representation by those nineteenth-century artists who made their living primarily from caricature, satire, and humorous illustrations. These range from the often astringent political and social commentary of Daumier (no. 13, illustrated, p. 31) and Willette (no. 93, illustrated, p. 41) to the charming scenes of the Parisian demi-monde by Steinlen (no. 85, illustrated, p. 40), Guys (no. 40, illustrated, p. 32),

Gavarni (nos. 30-33, illustrated, p. 31), and Forain (no. 22). Of course the greatest master in this field was Henri de Toulouse-Lautrec, who devoted much of his talent to recording a small circle of popular entertainers of the period. It is most likely one of these actress/dancer/singers known as Mademoiselle Lender, with her distinctive bun of hair and pointed chin, who is captured in a remarkable rapid pen and ink caricature by Lautrec (no. 88, illustrated, p. 36).[39] Also worthy of note is Maxime DeThomas, Lautrec's close friend of the 1890s, whom he called "le Grosnarbre" (big as a tree) and who also devoted himself to subjects of the Parisian theater and streets rendered in a rather more robust manner (no. 20, illustrated, p. 38).[40]

The great sculptors David d'Angers (Pierre-Jean David) and Auguste Rodin were among the outstanding artists of France during the nineteenth century, and they are appropriately represented in the Schlossberg collection by both drawings and sculpture. David d'Angers was more involved with the great personalities of his era than any other artist. His preliminary design (dated 1841) of a bas-relief was for the proposed tomb of Madame d'Abrantès (no. 15, illustrated, p. 30). She had been the mistress of Metternich, the wife of general Junot, a patron of Balzac, and a writer of trenchant memoirs covering the period from the Revolution through Napoleon and the Restoration, but she had died in poverty. Although never executed, the composition—which is also known from a drawing in the Musée Bonnat at Bayonne—shows the seated Madame d'Abrantès in profile, pausing for inspiration as the famous men of France gather in homage at the left.[41] Rodin, unlike David d'Angers, did not use drawing solely as a means of preparing his sculpture, but rather as a soothing escape from the trials of sculpting. His many sinuous and often erotic drawings of women done with pencil and watercolor (no. 72, illustrated, p. 27) are, as the younger sculptor Antoine Bourdelle observed, "as bold and as pure as a Greek amphora."[42]

## SCULPTURE

David d'Angers was born in 1788 in Angers, which he appended to his name to avoid confusion with the painter after he arrived in Paris in 1808. While he did not complete the bas-relief tomb of Madame d'Abrantès, he did successfully carry out many other projects during the course of his long career, and he frequently made reduced bronze versions of these. In 1828 he had been commissioned by the city of Marseilles to provide a relief for its monumental triumphal arch (also known as the Porte d'Aix), and for the vault on its west facade he designed the patriotic theme of *The Motherland Calling her Children to the Defense of Liberty*.[43] His crowded composition adds to the ancient relief tradition a rough vigor, as the citizens of Provence and even their pets flock to answer the call. A bronze rendering of the head of the central standing man from this relief (no. 114, illustrated, p. 54) is in the Schlossberg collection. Another remarkable work of David d'Angers's early career was the *Monument to Bonchamps*, completed in 1825. This had special meaning to the artist, for the subject was a military general whose forces had defeated and captured a large number of republican soldiers but who when mortally wounded in 1793 pardoned all these prisoners, among whom was the artist's father. For the marble tomb monument the sculptor depicted the general in the act of making his magnanimous gesture as an idealized young man, a secular John the Baptist, whose pose is derived from a figure on the Parthenon.[44] In the reduced bronze replica (no. 104, illustrated, p. 55), the figure is shown without the tomb base, which also had reliefs by the sculptor.

There are two other bronze reductions of major pieces by David d'Angers in the Schlossberg collection. The original marble of the *Philopomene*, commissioned by the French government for the Tuileries Gardens in 1832, is now in the Louvre. The subject was a patriotic Greek general, who according to Plutarch pulled out a spear which had pierced his thigh before leading his forces to victory.[45] The small but finely cast bronze (no. 108, illustrated, p. 55) conveys the power of the marble's heroic conception but adds to it the delight of a glistening surface. A piece which David d'Angers would have liked to have seen in large format atop the Arc de Triomphe in Paris was his *Liberty* of 1839. This he never achieved, but through widespread dispersal as a bronze (no. 109, illustrated, p. 55), it became one of his most popular creations.[46]

David d'Angers remains best remembered for his portraits of famous contemporaries—both three-dimensional busts such as those of Balzac (no. 110, illustrated, p. 54) and Bérenger (no. 111, illustrated, p. 54), and even more for his portrait medallions. Beginning in 1815 he produced more than five hundred medallions, creating what he called his "Gallery of Great Men."[47] On view here we have some of his most striking portrait medallions, representing Victor Hugo (no. 105), Paganini

(no. 107), Kléber (no. 112), and as proof that he was at least in some ways politically correct, Madame Récamier (no. 113).

One of the portrait medallions by David d'Angers depicts the short-lived painter Théodore Géricault (no. 106, illustrated, p. 54), by whom we have seen an early drawing (no. 33). Géricault also produced a small number of sculptures, including the problematic work called in French *L'Ecorché* (a dissected body), which is known in several plaster and bronze versions (no. 118, illustrated, p. 53). Lorenz Eitner, while noting that Géricault, in connection with his large painting *The Raft of the Medusa*, is reported to have made some small wax figures, has observed, "it is possible that all these various casts [of *L'Ecorché*] derive, perhaps at second hand, from a wax original by Géricault, but more than that one cannot well assert."[48]

Much clearer to us is the talent of the professional sculptors who flourished in France during the Second Empire. The most renowned of these, due to the fame of his allegorical group *The Dance* on the façade of the Paris Opera, is Jean-Baptiste Carpeaux. He was also a skilled portraitist, as is shown by the plaster bust of the artist Eugène Giraud (no. 95, illustrated, p. 57) and the bronze of the foundry owner Victor Thiébaut (no. 96, illustrated, p. 56).[49] A contemporary who also made a reputation for erotic subject matter and portraits of the famous was Auguste Clésinger. His *Tragedy* (no. 102) is actually a portrait of Rachel, the greatest tragedienne of the day shown in her most famous role, Phaedra.[50] Another successful sculptor of both public monuments and sensuous nudes was the Swiss-born Jean-Jacques (called James) Pradier. His elegant manner is certainly evident in the bronze reduction of one of his most famous works, *Sappho* (no. 123, illustrated, p. 56). The poetess of antiquity, her lyre resting behind her, seems lost in meditation. Her very chic air, however, derives from the fact that Pradier based his figure on the blonde poetess Louise Colet, who became the mistress of Flaubert. A large bronze of the subject was exhibited at the Salon of 1848 and a marble in 1852.[51]

The sculptor Alexandre Charpentier, it will be remembered, was the subject of a drawing by Henri Martin (no. 52), and his own art nouveau style is well represented by a bronze bas-relief of a mother and child (no. 97) and two plaquettes of languid women (nos. 100, 101). In addition there is a portrait plaque of the Belgian artist Constantin-Emile Meunier (no. 99). Characteristic of the cross references in which the Schlossberg collection abounds, this exhibition displays both a powerful bronze *Self-Portrait* by Meunier (no. 120) and a charcoal drawing of his favored subject, the coal miner (no. 55, illustrated, p. 39).

This overlap of draughtsmen and sculptors is also seen among the Impressionist and Post-Impressionist artists. Jean-François Raffaëlli made a small number of bronzes devoted to the humble types of individuals that he favored in his paintings and pastels. The bust of a man (no. 124, illustrated, p. 59) is the same head he employed for a full-length bronze titled *Bonhomme assis sur un banc*.[52] Paul Gauguin, on the other hand, had a long interest in carving that resulted in a great many sculpted works. During the winter of 1894-95 he was experimenting in the studio of the master ceramicist Ernest Chaplet and produced a so-called *Mask of a Savage* nearly identical to the face of the idol of the Polynesian earth god Fatu in his 1893 painting *The Moon and the Earth*. From this ceramic face Gauguin took a plaster cast which he painted (now in the Phillips Family Collection). In a letter of 1897 to the dealer Ambroise Vollard, Gauguin suggested that a bronze edition of the work be made, stating, "I am convinced that you would easily find thirty collectors who would pay 100 francs apiece."[53] Only two casts seem to have been made of this mask, which closely resembles Gauguin himself. These are in the Musée d'Orsay in Paris and the one (formerly in the collection of Walter P. Chrysler, Jr., sold after his death) now in the Schlossberg collection (no. 117, illustrated, p. 59).[54] Although small, it is a work of great, even frightening, intensity, haunting in the way it melds a "savage" face with the cultivated tradition of European bronzes.

The final three pieces of sculpture to be noted are all by great French masters of the late nineteenth century. Jules Dalou, the son of a Parisian glovemaker, was discovered by Carpeaux. His radical politics made it necessary for him to flee in 1871 to London, where he achieved success. When allowed to return to France in 1879, Dalou received a number of important official commissions. The small bronze of the Marquis de Lafayette (no. 103) is derived from one of these projects, for which Dalou competed while still in England in 1880. This was to be a grandiose monument at Versailles commemorating the Constituent Assembly of 1789 and was to consist of both a relief and four statues of heroic men. Although not carried out as intended, Dalou's relief was cast and placed in the Palais Bourbon. He had also sculpted the figures of Mirabeau and Lafayette; the former was purchased by the State but the artist retained the Lafayette, which became popu-

lar through a Sèvres porcelain reduction. The casting of the work in bronze was undoubtedly done after the artist's death, during the years 1902-05,[55] when his estate authorized limited editions. It is a noble piece which retains a good deal of Dalou's characteristic tactile modeling.

By far the most acclaimed sculptor of the era was Auguste Rodin, and one of his most monumental projects was a commission from the French government in 1880 for a huge set of bronze doors for the new Musée des arts decoratives. He first conceived an illustration to Dante's *Inferno*, but his subject gradually grew to include themes from mythology and others of his own imagining. In preparation for this vast work, Rodin made many small plaster models. One of the classical subjects that he considered for possible inclusion was Ovid's tale of the jealous cyclops Polyphemus discovering his beloved, the nymph Galatea, embracing the shepherd Acis. The subject provided the opportunity for the sculptor to combine two of his favorite motifs—a sensuously intertwined couple and a heroic male torso. Two versions of the subject are now known, one in the Rodin Museum in Philadelphia[56] and the recently discovered example in the Schlossberg collection (no. 125, illustrated, p. 60). In the end, the sculptor incorporated only the figure of Polyphemus into the finished *Gates of Hell*.

One of the many younger sculptors trained in Rodin's studio was Emile-Antoine Bourdelle, who worked as a *practicien* for the master from 1893 to 1906. In 1893 the young artist received his first major commission. This was for a monument to the defenders of his hometown of Montauban during the war of 1870-71, formally known as *Le Monument aux Combattants et Défenseurs du Tarn-et-Garonne*. The scale and powerful thrust of Bourdelle's design owes a great deal to Rodin, who was one of the few to praise the work when it was unveiled in 1902. Bourdelle made nearly fifty head studies in preparation for the monument.[57] The artist's daughter has written of *Head of a Warrior* (no. 94, illustrated, p. 59), "It was never cast during his lifetime but the first cast was executed in 1966 and was supervised by my mother (who was his pupil) and by me. Father's bronzes are limited to 10 (8 + 2 *epreuves d'artiste*). So far there are only 7 bronzes of that head."[58] The example in the Schlossberg collection is number one.

One final note with regard to sculpture that links the nineteenth and twentieth centuries was Rodin's admiration of the first exhibition by the

15

young sculptor Aristide Maillol in 1902.[59] We too can admire Maillol's plangent treatment of the female torso in one of his many lovely sculptural red chalk drawings (no. 50, illustrated, p. 45).

## TWENTIETH-CENTURY DRAWINGS

The twentieth-century portion of the Schlossberg collection exhibited here is more international in its scope than was the nineteenth. It commences with two artists of the Germanic school who were both well steeped in the traditions of the earlier period. Adolf Rudolf Hirémy Hirschl had been born into a Jewish family in Hungary, but when he was still a child they immigrated to Vienna. There he received a scholarship to attend the Akademie der Bildenden Künste and was launched on a successful career as a painter of old-fashioned allegorical decoration. Having won a major prize in 1880, Hirémy Hirschl was able to spend the years 1882-84 in Rome, where he settled permanently in 1898.[60] His mastery of the academic style is clear in the preparatory drawing of a rustic violinist (no. 43). A more individual style was developed by the Berlin-born Adolph Menzel. He only briefly attended that city's Academy of Arts and learned primarily in his father's lithography shop and from the study of other artists that he admired, including the Frenchman Meissonier. Menzel was a fanatic draughtsman whose motto was "Alles *Zeichen* ist gut, *alles* Zeichnen noch besser" (All drawing is good, drawing *all* is better yet).[61] He produced innumerable insightful graphite figure studies which, like the present example (no. 54, illustrated, p. 42), are dated but the subject unidentified.

Surprisingly, Menzel was to serve as a model for a later German artist whose style is part of the twentieth-century movement known as Expressionism. This was George Grosz, who wrote: "I loved our great Menzel for his highly superior illustrations. . . . Degas considered him the only great German draughtsman of the day. . . . Being a popular illustrator, Menzel did not distort nor did he experiment arbitrarily. . . . He was normal and yet a great artist at the same time."[62] By contrast, Grosz observes of himself, "I was not able to express the simple and wholesome qualities that I admired so much. Everything I painted seemed to go just beyond its limitations. When I painted with water colors, they overflowed their bounds, The faces I drew were mostly middle-aged and uglier than I had intended. How I would have loved to be able to control the sweet, the dainty, the normal and the beautiful."[63] Fortunately,

Grosz's wish remained unfulfilled, for his unwholesome, often grotesque but always incisive vision of humanity made him the ideal chronicler of life in Germany between the wars. The large drawings shown here are set in two of his favorite locales—a crowded subway carriage (no. 38) and a bustling street (no. 39, illustrated, p. 49).

The twentieth-century's struggle with the evil and madness in the world, given such potent expression in Grosz's work, took quite different forms with other artists. Georges Rouault, born in Paris during the city's bombardment in 1871, produced some equally grotesque visions of life but then turned to religious images, influenced by his early days as an apprentice stained glass maker. Rouault also found inspiration in the great symbolist poets of the nineteenth century. Such is the case of the little design (no. 73, illustrated, p. 46) in the black lithographic ink known as *touche* that he prepared as one of his many illustrations of Baudelaire's famous cycle *Les Fleurs du mal*.[64] This one—never actually executed as a lithograph—is entitled *A une dame créole (To a Creole Woman)* and was a voluptuous paean to Baudelaire's mistress, Jeanne Duval, in which the poet revels in her exotic features.[65]

The disturbing events of the twentieth century caused many artists to leave their homelands and seek asylum abroad. George Grosz, for example, was fortunate to be invited in 1932 to teach in New York. The Russian-born painter Pavel Tchelitchew also arrived there in 1934, after spending time in Germany and France. He had been a member of a group of artists labeled "Neo-Romantics," but in fact his art owed more to surrealism, and he rendered his often disturbing visions with an almost photographic precision. His reaction to his new country and memories of his past were all brought together in the complex painting *Phenomena*, conceived in 1935 and completed in the spring of 1938. Many of the phenomena that Tchelitchew incorporated into this work were mad and deformed people that he studied at the Freak Museum on 14th Street in New York.[66] Having mastered the renaissance technique of silverpoint, he was able to achieve in his many preparatory drawings for this painting a paradoxical contrast between his refined line and the bizarre subject matter (no. 86, illustrated, p. 46).

Expressionism and Surrealism, as represented by Grosz and Tchelitchew, were of course but two manifestations of the twentieth-century spirit. Most of the other key movements of the era take us back to Paris. Since, as we have already observed, the Schlossbergs prefer recognizable figural forms, there is to be found here only a brief nod to the abstracting principles of Cubism. Two French artists, who to different degrees developed this approach, are included. The more revolutionary was Albert Gleizes, whose cubistic *Crucifixion* is in the collection, but who is here represented by a more recently acquired study, *The Market at Courbevoie* (no. 35, illustrated, p. 47), which is related to his early, still representational paintings of 1905-1908.[67] The other painter, Roger de la Fresnaye, first studied at the Académie Julian in Paris, where one of his teachers was Sérusier, but by 1910-11 the young artist turned from the rather dated Nabi style to the revolutionary cubist idiom that had been created by Picasso and Braque and then adopted by Gleizes and others. The modified schematic treatment of the human form in which de la Fresnaye indulged at this time can be seen in his pen sketch *L'Ecossaise débout* (no. 24, illustrated, p. 48). By the 1920s de la Fresnaye had returned to a more traditional manner and often did realistic studies of his friends, to which he would intermittently, and with often humorous results, apply the cubists' disintegration of form (no. 25, illustrated, p. 48).[68]

The protean figure in twentieth-century art was Pablo Picasso, who in his career united aspects of expressionism, surrealism, and cubism and was a prolific draughtsman in the great European tradition.[69] This is made abundantly clear by his three drawings, which bring the exhibition to a close. Picasso's ability to transform a figure, in a consecutive series of studies, from an almost Ingres-like purity to a powerful distorted vision is evident here in his depiction of a melancholy young man (no. 60, illustrated, p. 50), while his child-like humor is revealed in a clever creation like the double-sided mask (no. 61), and finally his joyous rapture in the erotic surges forth in the energized lines of *The Kiss* (no. 59, illustrated, p. 50).

## NOTES

1. See Anita Brookner, *Greuze* (London, 1972), pl. 35.
2. See Antoine Schnapper and Arlette Sérrulaz, *Jacques Louis David 1748-1825* (Paris: Musée du Louvre, 1989), pp. 419-420.
3. See Antoine Schnapper, *David temoin de son temps* (Paris, 1980), p. 225, fig. 132; and Eric Zafran in *The Forsyth Wickes Collection in the Museum of Fine Arts* (Boston, 1992), pp. 105-106, no. 50.
4. See Schnapper and Sérrulaz (1989), pp. 534-539.
5. See Helmut von Erffa and Allen Staley, *The Paintings of Benjamin West* (New Haven, 1986), no. 422. Another lion study by West is in the Delaware Art Museum, Wilmington; see ibid., p. 224, note 7. Lions appear in other works by West, such as *Monument to Lord Nelson, The Mortality of Nelson, Death on a Pale Horse,* and *The Disobedient Prophet.* See Erffa and Staley (1986), nos. 110 and 111, and also *The World of Benjamin West,* exhib. cat. (Allentown, Pa.: The Allentown Art Museum, 1962), pls. 16 and 21.
6. Eugène-Emmanuel Amaury-Duval, *L'atelier d'Ingres* (Paris, 1878; Paris: Arthena, 1993).
7. See Marie-Madeleine Aubrun, *Henri Lehmann 1814-1882* (Paris, 1984), pp. 211-215, no. D893; and *Henri Lehmann 1814-1882, Portraits et decors parisiens,* exhib. cat. (Paris: Musée Carnavalet, 1983), pp. 117-119.
8. See Marie-Madeleine Aubrun, *Léon Bénouville, 1821-1859: Catalogue raisonée de l'oeuvre* (Paris, 1981), pp. 151-170.
9. See Albert Boime, *The Academy and French Painting in the Nineteenth Century* (London, 1971), pp. 22-23.
10. See Jean Claparede, *Montpellier, Musée Fabre, Dessins de la collection Alfred Bruyas et autres dessins des XIXe et XXe siècles* (Paris, 1962), no. 57; Maurice Sérrulaz, *Mémorial de l'exposition Eugène Delacroix* (Paris, 1963), p. 283, nos. 377-378; and Lee Johnson, *The Paintings of Eugène Delacroix, A Critical Catalogue* (Oxford, 1989), vol. V, p. 50.
11. See Maurice and Arlette Sérrulaz, *Dessins d'Eugène Delacroix 1798-1863,* in *Inventaire general des dessins école française* (Paris: Musée du Louvre, 1984), vol. II, pp. 69-71, nos. 1418-1422.
12. See *Géricault,* exhib. cat. (Paris: Grand Palais, 1991), p. 351, under no. 80, where the source was located in Jean-Baptiste Wicar, *Tableaux . . . de la Galerie de Florence* (Paris, 1789), vol. I, pl. 24.
13. See *Ernest Meissonier, Retrospective,* exhib. cat. (Lyon: Musée des Beaux-Arts de Lyon, 1993).
14. See Eric M. Zafran, *Cavaliers and Cardinals* (Cincinnati: Taft Museum of Art, 1992), pp. 13-22.
15. Jules Claretie, *Peintres et sculpteurs contemporains, deuxieme serie* (Paris, 1884), p. 133.
16. See Roger Peyre, "Jean-Jacques Henner," *L'Art et Les Artistes,* September 1905, ill. p. 220; Isabelle de Lannoy, *Musée national Jean-Jacques Henner, Catalogue des peintures* (Paris, 1990), pp. 171-173; and Shepherd Gallery, *French and Other European Drawings . . .* (New York: 1981-82), no. 114. The painting is now in the Musée Henner, Paris, and the large finished drawing has been in the collection of the Los Angeles County Museum of Art since 1991.

17. For the painting (ca. 1863, oil on canvas, location unknown), see Michael Wentworth, *James Tissot* (Oxford: Clarendon Press, 1984), pl. 16; the Schlossberg drawing is also illustrated (pl. 17).

18. See *Edouard Manet*, exhib. cat. (Philadelphia: Philadelphia Museum of Art, 1966), no. 147. On the proper spelling of his name, see Anne Coffin Hanson, *Manet and The Modern Tradition* (New Haven, 1977), p. 163.

19. See John Rewald, "Auguste Renoir and his brother," in *Studies in Impressionism*, ed. Irene Gordon and Frances Weitzenhoffer (New York, 1985), pp. 22-23.

20. François Daulte, Sotheby's, New York, sales catalogue, May 20, 1987, no. 73.

21. *Works of Jean F. Raffaelli* (New York: The American Art Galleries, 1895).

22. Theodore Child, "The Hôtel Drouot," *Harper's New Monthly Magazine*, February 1889, p. 331.

23. Richard R. Brettell, letter to Dr. Michael Schlossberg, April 15, 1991. See Richard Bretell, et al., *The Art of Paul Gauguin*, exhib. cat. (Washington, D.C.: National Gallery of Art, 1988), pp. 36-37, no. 13. Courbet's *Self-Portrait with Cello* of 1847, exhibited in the Salon of the following year, is now in the National Museum, Stockholm. See *Gustave Courbet, 1819-1877*, exhib. cat. (Paris: Grand Palais, 1977), no. 16.

24. Richard R. Brettell, letter to Dr. Michael Schlossberg, April 15, 1991.

25. Caroline Boyle-Turner, conversation with author, November 29, 1993.

26. See Robert Goldwater, *Paul Gauguin* (New York, 1972), pp. 148-149 and 158-159.

27. Ibid., pp. 138-139.

28. See René Porro, *Claude-Emile Schuffenecker 1851-1934* (Combeaufontaine, 1992), fig. 122. A nearly identical study is in the collection of the Fogg Art Museum, Cambridge, Ma., and another head study of Bernard by Schuffenecker sold at Sotheby's, New York, November 21, 1980, no. 140.

29. See *Emile Bernard 1868-1941, A Pioneer of Modern Art*, exhib. cat. (Amsterdam: Van Gogh Museum, 1990), p. 248, fig. 106.

30. This particular Ibels is similar to a pastel he made of a café-concert performer in 1892. See Patricia Eckert Boyer, ed., *The Nabis and the Parisian Avant-Garde* (New Brunswick, N.J., 1988), no. 62. Also see Philip Dennis Cate, ed., *The Graphic Arts and French Society, 1871-1914* (New Brunswick, 1988), pp. 144-158.

31. See John Russell, *Edouard Vuillard 1869-1940*, exhib. cat. (Toronto: Art Gallery of Ontario, 1971), p. 62.

32. That Ranson was in Brittany in the summer of 1891 is evident from letters he sent from there to the painter Jan Verkade. See Caroline Boyle-Turner, *Jan Verkade Disciple hollandaise de Gauguin*, exhib. cat. (Amsterdam: Rijksmuseum Vincent van Gogh, 1989), p. 128. See also *Die Nabis, Propheten der Moderne*, exhib. cat. (Zurich: Kunsthaus, 1993), pp. 477 and 493, n. 78.

33. Clive Bell, *Old Friends Personal Recollections* (London, 1956), p. 166.

34. This drawing is close to the painting entitled *Promontory, Brittany* in the Bristol Museums and Art Gallery. See Jonathan Benington, *Roderic O'Conor, A Biography with a Catalogue of his Work* (Dublin, 1992), p. 197, no. 65, fig. 27.

35. On Angrand's *Maternités* exhibited at Durand Ruel's in 1899 and at the Salon des Indépendants in 1905, see *Charles Angrand 1854-1926*, exhib. cat. (Château-Musée de Dieppe, 1976), nos. 20-22.

36. P. Adam, "La Presse et le symbolisme," *Le Symboliste*, October 7, 1886.

37. See "Salon des Artistes français," *L'Art et Les Artistes*, III, September 1906, p. 126; *Peintres d'aujourd'hui, Henri Martin, sa vie, son oeuvre* (Paris, 1910), n.p.; and *Henri Martin 1860-1943*, exhib. cat. (Toulouse: Palais des Arts, 1983), p. 64. The painting is now in the Musée de Picardie in Amiens.

38. See Jacques Daurelle, Camille Mauclair, et al., *Armand Point et son Oeuvre* (Paris, 1901), p. 33. In *French Symbolist Painters*, exhib. cat. (London: Hayward Gallery, 1972), the drawing is identified as a head of Madame Berthelot.

39. The most convincing comparison is with the lithograph *Lender Taking a Bow* of 1895. See Götz Adriani, *Toulouse-Lautrec: The Complete Graphic Works* (London, 1988), pp. 157-158, no. 114.

40. See Theodore Reff, *Manet and Modern Paris*, exhib. cat. (Washington, D.C.: National Gallery of Art, 1982), pp. 126-127.

41. See *Dessins français du XIXe siècle du Musée Bonnat à Bayonne*, exhib. cat. (Paris: Musée du Louvre, 1979), p. 40, no. 44. David d'Angers did in fact execute a plaster medallion of the head of Madame d'Abrantès. See Viviane Huchard, *Galerie David D'Angers* (Musées d'Angers, 1989), p. 126.

42. See Elisabeth Chase Geissbühler, *Rodin Later Drawings with Interpretations by Antoine Bourdelle* (London, 1963), p. 62.

43. See Huchard (1989), pp. 92-93; and Jacques de Caso, *David d'Angers* (Princeton, N.J., 1992), pp. 136-139.

44. Huchard (1989), pp. 34-35, and de Caso (1992), pp. 62-71.

45. Huchard (1989), p. 63. See also Peter Fusco and H. W. Janson, eds., *The Romantics to Rodin*, exhib. cat. (Los Angeles, 1980), pp. 222-223, no. 101.

46. Huchard (1989), p. 116; and *The Art of the July Monarchy, France 1830 to 1848*, exhib. cat. (Columbia, Mo.: Museum of Art and Archaeology, University of Missouri, 1990), pp. 231-232, no. 37.

47. Fusco and Janson (1980), pp. 216-217.

48. Lorenz Eitner, letter to David Yates, December 21, 1987.

49. For Thiébault, see *Jean-Baptiste Carpeaux, Sa Famille et ses amis*, exhib. cat. (Courbevoie: Musée Roybet-Fould, 1976), no. 31; and Anne Middleton Wagner, *Jean-Baptiste Carpeaux* (New Haven, 1986), pp. 182, 201, and 300.

50. On the actress Rachel, see the portrait of her by Amaury-Duval in *The Second Empire, Art in France under Napoleon III*, exhib. cat. (Philadelphia: Philadelphia Museum of Art, 1978), p. 249, no. VI-1; see also Rachel M. Brownstein, *Tragic Muse, Rachel of the Comédie Française* (New York, 1993), p. 180.

51. See *Nineteenth Century French Sculpture: Monuments for the Middle Class*, exhib. cat. (Louisville, Ky.: J. B. Speed Art Museum, 1971), pp. 208-209; and *Statues de chair: sculptures de James Pradier, 1790-1852*, exhib. cat. (Geneva: Musée d'art et d'histoire, 1985), pp. 171-178.

52. See Arsène Alexandre, *Jean-François Raffaëlli: Peintre, Graveur, et Sculpteur* (Paris, 1909), pp. 165-170.

53. Quoted in Brettell (1988), p. 367.

54. See ibid., pp. 367-369, nos. 209-210a.

55. See Fusco and Janson (1980), pp. 192-193, no. 74.

56. See John L. Tancock, *The Sculpture of August Rodin: The Collection of the Rodin Museum* (Philadelphia, 1976), p. 210, no. 22. A plaster of the single figure of Polyphemus is in the Maryhill collection; see *Rodin: The Maryhill Collection*, exhib. cat. (Pullman, Wa.: Museum of Art, Washington State University, 1976), p. 33, no. 18.

57. See Peter Canon-Brooks, *Emile-Antoine Bourdelle, An Illustrated Commentary* (London, 1983), pp. 22-28.

58. Rhodia Dufet Bourdelle, letter to Dr. Michael Schlossberg, December 10, 1990.

59. Rodin is reported to have said, "In all of modern sculpture, I don't know a piece which is so absolutely beautiful as the *Leda* [of Maillol]; it is certainly a chef-d'oeuvre." Quoted in *Hommage à Aristide Maillol (1861-1944)*, exhib. cat. (Paris: Musée National d'Art Moderne, 1961), p. 10.

60. See *Adolf Hirémy Hirschl*, exhib. cat. (Rome: Galeria Carlo Virgilio, 1981); *Adolf Hirémy-Hirschl 1860-1933, The Beauty of Decline*, exhib. cat. (Chicago: Roger Ramsay Gallery, Inc., 1984); and *Adolf Hirémy Hirschl 1860-1933*, exhib. cat. (London: Matthiesen Fine Art, Ltd., 1987).

61. See *Adolph Menzel 1815-1905, Master Drawings from East Berlin*, exhib. cat. (New York: The Frick Collection, 1990), p. 12.

62. George Grosz, *A Little Yes and a Big No, The Autobiography of George Grosz*, trans. Lola Sachs Dorin (New York, 1946), p. 325.

63. Ibid.

64. See Richard Nathanson and Jacques Guignard, *Georges Rouault, 1871-1958, Paintings and Fourteen Aquatints for Les Fleurs du Mal*, exhib. cat. (London: Eskenazi Ltd., 1972). See also François Chapon, *The Illustrated Books by Rouault* (Milan, 1992), pp. 36-49.

65. The first edition of Baudelaire's *Les Fleurs du mal* was published in 1857. The poem "A une dame creole" was no. LXIV. Baudelaire had met Jeanne Duval in 1842 and a well-known portrait of her, painted by Manet in 1862, is now in Budapest.

66. See James Thrall Soby, *Tchelitchew, Paintings, Drawings*, exhib. cat. (New York: The Museum of Modern Art, 1942), p. 29, figs. 51-53; and Parker Tyler, *The Divine Comedy of Pavel Tchelitchew* (New York, 1967), pp. 387-409.

67. See *Albert Gleizes 1881-1953, A Retrospective Exhibition*, exhib. cat. (New York: The Solomon R. Guggenheim Museum, 1964), no. 5.

68. See, for example, the various studies of Jean Cocteau of 1921 in Germain Seligman, *Roger de la Fresnaye* (London, 1969), p. 248.

69. See, for example, Jakob Rosenberg, *Great Draughtsmen from Pisanello to Picasso* (Cambridge, Ma., 1959), pp. 121-137.

# ILLUSTRATIONS: DRAWINGS

92. Benjamin West, *Lion*

37. Jean-Baptiste Greuze, *Seated Woman with an Open Book,*
*Study for "The Paralytic"*

18. Eugène Delacroix, *Studies after
    Michelangelo*

33. Théodore Géricault, *Bacchus
    and Ariadne on the Back of
    a Leopard*

66. Armand Point, *Portrait of Madame Berthelot*

75. Theo Van Rysselberghe, *Mother and Child*

22. Jean-Louis Forain, *In the Wings*

5. Emile Bernard, *Fête Galante*

72.  August Rodin, *Woman*

81.  Georges Seurat, *Study of Soldiers*

14. Jacques-Louis David, *Portrait of the Poet Le Brun*

21. Hippolyte Flandrin, *Portrait of a Seated Woman*

45. Jean-Auguste-Dominique Ingres,
*Study of Cloaks*

36. Jean-Baptiste Greuze, *Head of a Boy*

17. Eugène Delacroix, *Study for
"Michelangelo and his Genius"*

15. David D'Angers, *Study for a Tomb Relief for
the Duchess D'Abrantès*

19. Jules Elie Delaunay, *Studies after Raphael*

13. Honoré Daumier, *Pluto*

32. Paul Gavarni, *Partis en Guerre Tour tuer les ennemis*

31. Paul Gavarni, *Un Portrait Flatté*

40. Ernest-Hyacinthe-Constantin Guys,
    *Dames de la Halle*

53. Jean-Louis-Ernest Meissonier, *Studies for the
    "Livre du Mariage"*

87. Jacques-Joseph Tissot, *Preparatory Study for "The Departure of the Prodigal Son from Venice"*

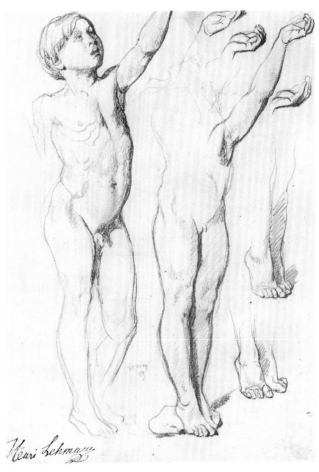

47. Henri Lehmann, *Studies of a Young Boy, Standing Nude*

48. Léon Augustin Lhermitte, *Portrait of an Old Woman*

42. Jean Jacques Henner, *Saint Sebastian tended by Saint Irene*

51. Edouard Manet, *Portrait of Henri Vignaux*

70. Pierre Auguste Renoir, *Drawing after Manet's "Fifer"*

88.  Henri de Toulouse-Lautrec, *Mademoiselle Lender[?]*

44.  Henri-Gabriel Ibels, *Portrait of Madame Jeanne Bloch*

64. Camille Pissarro, *Child at Table (Ludovic-Rodolphe?)*

65. Camille Pissarro, *The Family of the Artist*

83. Alfred Sisley, *Landscape*

90. Jehan Georges Vibert,
*The Knife Grinder*

20. Maxime DeThomas, *Seated Man Holding an Umbrella*

71. Théodule Augustin Ribot,
*Portrait of the Artist's
Daughter*

8. Léon Bonnat, *Portrait of Auguste Nadaud*

9. François Bonvin, *Portrait of a Man, and Study of a Hand*

55. Constantin Emile Meunier, *Portrait of a Miner*

85. Théophile Steinlen, *Illustration from "Gil Blas"*

67. Jean-François Raffaëlli, *À l'Hôtel des Ventes, Salle Drouot, Paris (Broker in the Mazas, Hôtel Drouot)*

93. Adolphe Léon Willette, *La République eclairant le monde . . . des fonctionnaires*

79. Georges Seurat, *Ulysses and the Suitors*

54. Adolf von Menzel,
*Study of a Man's Head*

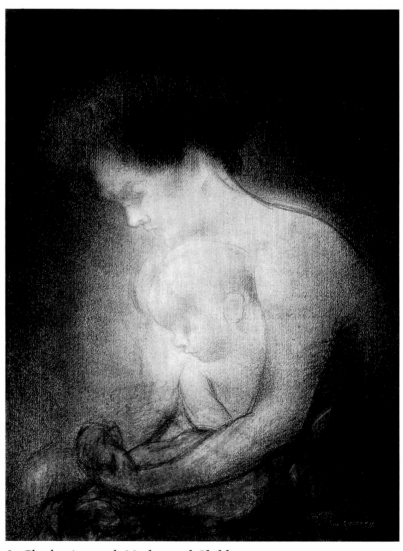

3. Charles Angrand, *Mother and Child*

29. Paul Gauguin, *Sleeping Child*    27. Paul Gauguin, *Study of a Cellist*

69. Paul Ranson, *Brittany Landscape*

77.  Paul Sérusier, *Sketches of Gauguin and Ranson*

78.  Paul Sérusier, *Studies of Breton Peasant Women*

50. Aristide Maillol, *Seated Woman*

56. Amedeo Modigliani, *Figure in a Turban*
    *(Portrait of Nijinski?)*

73. Georges Rouault, *To a Creole Woman*

86. Pavel Tchelitchew, *Mad Woman*

58. Jules Pascin, *Café Scene*, Paris

35. Albert Gleizes, *Market at Courbevoie*

25. Roger de la Fresnaye, *Portraits of a Man*

24. Roger de la Fresnaye, *L'Écossaise Debout*

39. George Grosz, *Berlin Street Scene*

60. Pablo Picasso, *Bust of a Man*

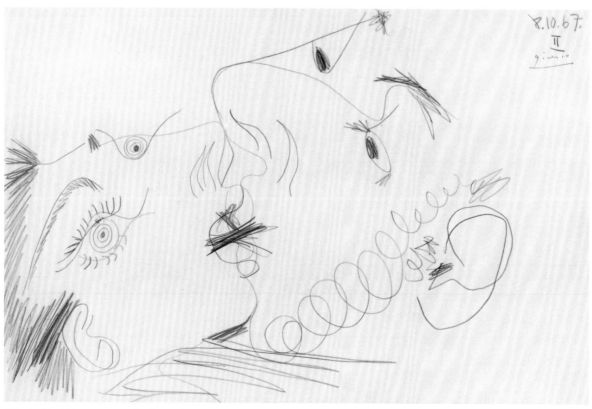

59. Pablo Picasso, *Study for "The Kiss"*

# ILLUSTRATIONS: SCULPTURE

118.  Théodore Géricault, *L'Ecorché*

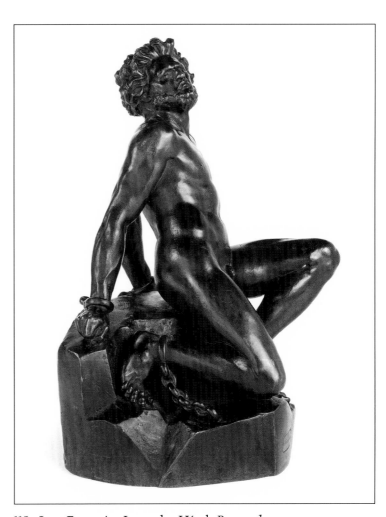

119.  Jean-Françoise Legendre-Héral, *Prometheus*

110. David D'Angers, *Balzac*

111. David D'Angers, *Bérenger*

106. David D'Angers,
*Géricault Pictor*

114. David D'Angers, *Study for the West Facade of
the Arc de Triomphe* [Marseilles]

104. David D'Angers, *Bonchamps*

108. David D'Angers, *Philopomene*

109. David D'Angers, *Liberty*

116. Jean-François-Marie Garnier, *L'Enfer des Luxurieux*

97. Alexandre-Louis-Marie Charpentier,
*Mother and Child*

124. Jean-François Raffaëlli, *Study for
"Bonhomme assis sur un Banc"*

94. Emile-Antoine Bourdelle, *Head of a Warrior*

117. Paul Gauguin, *Mask of a Savage*

96. Jean-Baptiste Carpeaux, *Portrait of Victor Thiébaut*

123. Jean-Jacques Pradier, *Sappho*

95. Jean-Baptiste Carpeaux, *Eugène Giraud*

125. Auguste Rodin, *Polyphemus, Acis, and Galatea*

126. Victor Joseph Jean Ambroise Segoffin, *Philoctetes and the Sons of Asclepius*

# Catalogue of the Exhibition

Drawings and sculpture are listed separately, alphabetically by artist.

Dimensions are given in inches followed by centimeters in parentheses, height before width before depth.

Short titles are used in two instances in exhibition histories and references: *Drawings* (1981) refers to the exhibition and catalogue by Peter Morrin and Eric Zafran, *Drawings from Georgia Collections*, 19th and 20th Centuries (Atlanta: High Museum of Art, May 14-June 28, 1981); *Georgia Collects* (1989) refers to the exhibition and catalogue *Georgia Collects* (Atlanta: High Museum of Art, January 24-March 6, 1989, and travelling).

Collectors' marks are referred to by Lugt number, from F. Lugt, *Les Marques de collections de dessins et d'estampes . . .* (Amsterdam, 1921).

## DRAWINGS

### Charles-Jean Agard (French, 1866-1942)
1. *Reclining Nude*
   Black chalk on cream-colored laid
   paper
   10¹/₁₆ x 18 (25.6 x 45.7)
   Signed, lower left: *Ch. Agard*

PROVENANCE: Marcel Flavian, Paris.

### Eugène-Emmanuel Pineu Amaury-Duval (French, 1808-1885)
2. *Portrait of a Man [Adolphe]*, 1834
   Graphite on off-white wove paper
   13³/₄ x 10³/₈ (34.9 x 26.4)
   Inscribed, center right: *À son ami
   Adolphe, Amaury-Duval 1834*

PROVENANCE: David and Constance
Yates, New York.

### Charles Angrand (French, 1854-1926)
3. *Mother and Child*, ca. 1899
   Charcoal heightened with white
   chalk
   24 x 17³/₄ (61 x 45.1)
   Signed, lower right: CH ANGRAND

PROVENANCE: O'Hana Gallery, Estate
of Jacques O'Hana, London; Sotheby
Parke Bernet, New York, sale, June 8,
1977, no. 15.

EXHIBITED: Charles Angrand, Château-
Musée de Dieppe, June 19-September
20, 1976, no. 20 (?); Drawings (1981),
no. 22.

REFERENCES: Drawings (1981), no. 22,
p. 50, illus. p. 51.

Illustrated, p. 42.

### François-Léon Bénouville (French, 1821-1859)
4. *Head of a Man*
   Graphite heightened with white on
   tan paper
   7 x 5⁷/₈ sight (17.8 x 14.9)
   Estate stamp?, lower left

PROVENANCE: Bruno de Bayser, Paris;
Private collection, New York.

This drawing is a study for the painting *Les Martyrs conduits au supplice*
(Paris, Louvre).

### Emile Bernard (French, 1868-1941)
5. *Fête Galante*, 1890
   Watercolor and colored chalks
   15 x 11¹/₂ (38.1 x 28.4)
   Signed and dated, lower right:
   Emile Bernard 90

PROVENANCE: Commandant Bernard-
Fort, Paris; Galerie Coligny, Paris.

Illustrated, p. 26.

### Alexandre Bida (French, 1823-1895)
6. *A Game of Chess*
   Graphite on gray-green paper
   9¹/₈ x 7³/₄ sight (23.2 x 19.7)
   Signed, lower right: *Bida*

PROVENANCE: Private collection,
Florida.

### Léon Bonnat (French, 1834-1922)
7. *Young Girl Reclining*, 1862
   Graphite, with white highlights, on
   paper partially squared in graphite
   6⁷/₈ x 10¹/₈ (17.5 x 25.7) sight
   Signed, lower left: *Bonnat 1862*

PROVENANCE: The Drawing Shop, New
York.

This drawing is a study for the painting
*La Pasqua Maria*, 1862.

8. *Portrait of Auguste Nadaud*, 1883
   Black ink on light brown wove
   paper
   9¹/₈ x 8¹/₂ (23.2 x 21.6)
   Signed, dedicated, dated, lower
   right: *à mon ami Nadaud/Ln
   Bonnat Novembre 1883*

EXHIBITED: *Georgia Collects* (1989).

REFERENCES: *Georgia Collects* (1989),
p. 200, illus. p. 52.

Illustrated, p. 39.

### François Bonvin (French, 1817-1887)
9. *Portrait of a Man, and Study of a
   Hand*
   Red and white chalk and charcoal
   6¹/₂ x 8 (16.5 x 20.3)
   Signed, lower right: *F Bonvin*

Illustrated, p. 39.

### Louis-Maurice Boutet De Monvel (French, 1851-1913)
10. *Cavalry Charge*, 1873
    Ink, gouache, and watercolor
    8³/₄ x 12³/₄ (22.2 x 32.4)
    Signed and dated, upper left:
    *MB de Monvel 1873*

PROVENANCE: Patrice Barbé, Paris.

### Eugène Carrière (French, 1849-1906)
11. *Studies of Figures*
    Recto: three male heads and arms,
    hand, isolated head
    Verso: woman and child at table
    Charcoal on buff paper
    12³/₁₆ x 9¹/₄ (31 x 23.5)
    Signed, lower right: *Eugène
    Carrière 1888*

PROVENANCE: A. M. Adler Fine Arts,
New York.

EXHIBITED: *Drawings* (1981), no. 109.

REFERENCES: *Drawings* (1981), no. 109,
p. 212.

### Pascal-Adolphe-Jean Dagnan-Bouveret (French, 1852-1929)
12. *Young Girl in a Bonnet*
    Graphite
    11 x 8¹/₄ (27.9 x 21)
    Signed, lower right: Pas Dagnan B.

PROVENANCE: Peter Silverman, Paris.

### Honoré Daumier (French, 1808-1879)
13. *Pluto*
    Graphite
    10³/₄ x 8¹/₈ (27.3 x 20.6)
    Initialed, lower left.

PROVENANCE: Obelisk Gallery, London; Sotheby's, London, sale, May 28, 1986, no. 23.

Illustrated, p. 31.

## Jacques-Louis David (French, 1748-1825)

14. *Portrait of the Poet Lebrun*
Graphite on pale blue-green laid paper
7¼ x 5⅝ (18.4 x 14.3)
Signed and annotated, lower right: *LeBrun le Poete Par David de Souvenir.*
Stamped, lower left: *G* [stamp for Gigoux collection]

PROVENANCE: Gigoux Collection; Private collection, Philadelphia.

EXHIBITED: *Georgia Collects* (1989).

REFERENCES: *Georgia Collects* (1989), p. 46 illus., and p. 200.

Illustrated, p. 28.

## David D'Angers [Pierre-Jean David] (French, 1788-1856)

15. *Study for a Tomb Relief for the Duchess D'Abrantès*, 1841
Soft graphite on papier calque laid on mulberry paper
8¹¹/₁₆ x 7⅞ (22.1 x 20 cm.)
Signed and inscribed in brown ink along bottom: *Projet de bas relief pour le monument de Mme. D'Abrantès. David* [with flourish] *1841*

PROVENANCE: Shepherd Gallery, New York.

EXHIBITED: *French Nineteenth Century Drawings, Watercolors, Paintings and Sculpture*, Shepherd Gallery, New York, Spring 1987, no. 61.

REFERENCES: Elisabeth Kashey and Robert Kashey, *French Nineteenth Century Drawings, Watercolors, Paintings and Sculpture* (New York: Shepherd Gallery, 1987), no. 61.

A drawing of the same subject, dated 1839, is in the collection of the Musée Bonnat in Bayonne, France. See *Dessins français du XIXe siècle du musée Bonnat à Bayonne* (Paris: Musée du Louvre, February 2-April 30, 1979), no. 44, p. 40.

Illustrated, p. 30.

## Edgar Degas (French, 1834-1917)

16. Recto and verso: *Studies from the Antique*
Graphite
9½ x 12¼ (24 x 31)
Stamped with the atelier mark, verso.

PROVENANCE: Sotheby's, London, sale, May 28, 1986, no. 22.

## Eugène Delacroix (French, 1798-1863)

17. *Study for "Michelangelo and his Genius"*
Graphite
8½ x 5¾ (21.6 x 14.6)
Estate stamp lower right.

PROVENANCE: Bruno de Bayser, Paris.

This drawing is a study for the ceiling decoration for the library of the Chamber of Deputies, Palais Bourbon, Paris.

Illustrated, p. 30.

18. *Studies after Michelangelo*, 1832
Red chalk
17½ x 11½ (44.5 x 29.2)

PROVENANCE: Jacques Fischer, Paris; Frederick J. Cummings, Detroit.

EXHIBITED: *Georgia Collects* (1989).

REFERENCES: *Georgia Collects* (1989), p. 201, illus. p. 52.

The upper figure is a study after the female figure of Dawn in the Medici Chapel in Florence. The lower figure is a sketch after Michelangelo's Adam in the Sistine Chapel in Rome.

Illustrated, cover, p. 24.

## Jules Elie Delaunay (French, 1828-1891)

19. *Studies after Raphael*
18⅛ x 8⅛ sight (46 x 20.6)
Graphite
Stamp, lower right: *Oeuvre Jules Elie Delaunay Dessins*

This drawing is a study of a portion of Raphael's Vatican fresco of *The Fire in the Borgo.*

Illustrated, p. 30.

## Maxime DeThomas (French, 1867-1939)

20. *Seated Man Holding an Umbrella*
Black chalk, watercolor, and pastel on light brown wove paper
28⅛ x 16¼ (71.4 x 41.3)

PROVENANCE: Giosi, Rome.

EXHIBITED: *Esquisses Ventiennes, Exposition à Dessins et Aquarelles de Maxime DeThomas*, Galeries de L'Art Decoratif, Paris, April 23-May 19, 1906.

Illustrated, p. 38.

## Hippolyte Flandrin (French, 1809-1864)

21. *Portrait of a Seated Woman*, 1848
Graphite on off-white medium-weight wove paper laid to cream medium-weight wove paper
14³/₁₆ x 9³/₁₆ (36 x 23.3)
Inscribed in graphite, lower left: *Paris, 1848*

PROVENANCE: Charles Moffett, New York; Robert Flynn-Johnson.

EXHIBITED: Middlebury College, Middlebury, Vt., Spring 1973; *Ingres and Delacroix through Degas and Puvis de Chavannes*, Shepherd Gallery, New York, Spring 1975, no. 63; *Füssli through Tiffany: 19th and Early 20th Century Paintings, Drawings and Sculpture*, Shepherd Gallery, New York, Fall 1987.

REFERENCES: Middlebury College, exhib. cat. (Middlebury, Vt., 1973), illus.; *Ingres and Delacroix through Degas and Puvis de Chavannes* (New York: Shepherd Gallery, 1975) no. 63, illus.; Elisabeth Kashey, *Füssli through Tiffany: 19th and Early 20th Century Paintings, Drawings and Sculpture* (New York: Shepherd Gallery, 1987), no. 9, illus.

Illustrated, p. 28.

## Jean-Louis Forain (French, 1852-1931)

22. *In the Wings*
Watercolor and graphite heightened with white gouache on gray paper
6⅛ x 8 (15.6 x 20.3)
Signed, lower right: *Forain*

PROVENANCE: Sotheby's, New York, sale, February 27, 1982, no. 90.

This scene was also the subject of a fan-shaped lithograph, *Pour le Bal Gavarni.* See Marcel Guérin, *J.-L. Forain Lithographe: Catalogue Raisonné de l'Oeuvre Lithographié de l'Artiste* (San Francisco, Alan Wofsy, 1980), no. 70.

Illustrated, p. 26.

23. *Portrait of Ambroise Vollard*
Graphite
9½ x 7¼ (24.1 x 18.4)
Signed, lower right: *Forain*

PROVENANCE: Gerald Schurr.

EXHIBITED: Musée Marmottan, Paris, May-June, 1978, no. 92.

REFERENCES: Exhib. cat. (Paris: Musée Marmottan, 1978), no. 92, p. 60.

## Roger de la Fresnaye (French, 1885-1925)

24. *L'Écossaise Debout*, ca. 1913
Pen and ink on paper lined at the edges with white paper
13⅛ x 10½ (34 x 26.5)
Estate stamp, lower right.

PROVENANCE: Anonymous sale, Sotheby's, London, December 3, 1958, no. 24; Leicester Galleries, London; Lefevre Gallery, London; Christie's East, New York, sale, April 18, 1983, no. 113.

REFERENCES: Germain Seligmann, *Roger de la Fresnaye, with a Catalogue Raisonné* (Greenwich, Conn.: New York Graphic Society Ltd., 1969), no. 236, p. 16 illus., and p. 183.

Illustrated, p. 48.

25. *Portraits of a Man*, 1921
Brush and India ink
10½ x 7⅞ (26.7 x 20)
Signed and dated in graphite, upper left: *Grasse '21 La fresnaye*

PROVENANCE: Paul Chadourne, Paris; Christie's, London, sale, December 6, 1983, no. 192.

EXHIBITED: *XVIIeme Exposition Internationale des Beaux-Arts*, Venice, 1930, no. 69b; *Roger de la Fresnaye*, Marie Harriman Gallery, New York, March 1932, no. 23; *Exhibition of Watercolours and Drawings by Roger de la Fresnaye*; Wildenstein & Co., London, April-May, 1936, no. 33; *Georgia Collects* (1989).

REFERENCES: Waldemar George, *Dessins et Gouaches (1919-25) de Roger de la Fresnaye* (Paris: Librairie de France, 1927); *Roger de la Fresnaye* (New York: Marie Harriman Gallery, 1932), no. 23; *Georgia Collects* (1989), p. 155 illus., and p. 213.

Illustrated, p. 48.

**Eugène Fromentin (French, 1820-1876)**
26. *Study of an Arab*
Graphite
4³/₄ x 3¹/₂ (12.1 x 8.9)
Estate stamp, lower right.

**Paul Gauguin (French, 1848-1903)**
27. Recto: *Study of a Cellist*, ca. 1881
Verso: *Study of a Sleeping Child and a Woman*
Charcoal on gray paper
11¹/₂ x 9¹/₁₆ (29 x23)

PROVENANCE: Pola Gauguin, Oslo; L. Latouche, Paris; Sotheby Parke Bernet, New York, sale, June 13, 1978, no. 9.

EXHIBITED: *Drawings* (1981), no. 23; *Georgia Collects* (1989).

REFERENCES: *Drawings* (1981), no. 23, pp. 52-53 illus.; *Georgia Collects* (1989), p. 61 illus., and p. 201.

The drawing on the recto is probably a self-portrait of the artist.

Illustrated, p. 43.

28. Recto and verso: *Studies*
Sanguine and black chalk on gray paper affixed to a mount
9 x 11¹/₂ (23 x 29)

PROVENANCE: Pola Gauguin, Oslo; Sotheby Parke Bernet, New York, sale, June 13, 1978, no. 10.

According to Pola Gauguin, the artist's son, this drawing was part of an album of 33 sketches by Paul Gauguin. (Statement, Oslo, October 24, 1929.)

29. Recto: *Sleeping Child*
Black chalk
Stamped (Lugt 2078) with monogram, lower right.
Verso: *Studies of a Leopard, Figures on Horseback, and Infants*
Graphite
10³/₄ x 7 (27.3 x 17.8)
Stamped with monogram.

PROVENANCE: Hugo Perls; Christie's, New York, sale, May 18, 1983, no. 107.

EXHIBITED: *Cent Oeuvres de Gauguin*, Galerie Charpentier, Paris, 1960, no. 99.

*Sleeping Child* may be a study for Gauguin's painting *Where Do You Come From? Who Are We? Where Are We Going?*, 1897 (Museum of Fine Arts, Boston). Diverse sketches on the verso appear to be related to other paintings by Gauguin: two figures on horseback recall figures in *The White Horse*, 1898 (Musée d'Orsay, Paris), and in *Riders on the Beach*, 1902 (Niarchos Collection). The animal at the bottom of the sheet is nearly the same as one in *Te rerioa (The Dream)*, 1897 (Courtauld Gallery, London), which also has a child asleep.

Illustrated, p. 43.

**Paul Gavarni [Guillaume-Sulpice Chevalier] (French, 1804-1866)**
30. *La Cuisinière*
Watercolor and gouache
12⁵/₈ x 8¹/₄ (32.1 x 21)
Signed, lower right: *Gavarni*
Inscription, along the bottom: *Je n'en ai pas de "Credit-Fonciers," moi! et j'ai été/tente sept ans cuisinière.*

PROVENANCE: B. Harrari; Beaux-Arts Gallery, London; E. Maurice Bloch; Christie's, New York, June 19, 1990, no. 155.

31. *Un Portrait Flatté*
Brown ink and wash on tan wove paper
7 x 9⁷/₁₆ (17.7 x 21.4)
Initialed, lower right: *G*
Inscription, lower center: *Un portrait flatté*

PROVENANCE: David and Constance Yates, New York.

Illustrated, p. 31.

32. *Partis en Guerre Tour tuer les ennemis*
Watercolor, gouache, pen and gray ink on light tan paper
13¹/₈ x 8¹/₄ (33.3 x 20.7 cm.)
Signed, lower right: *Gavarni*
Inscription, lower left: *Partis en guerre tour tuer les ennemis*

PROVENANCE: E. Maurice Bloch; Christie's, New York, sale, January 9, 1991, no. 62.

Illustrated, p. 31

**Théodore Géricault (French, 1791-1824)**
33. Recto: *Bacchus and Ariadne on the Back of a Leopard*
Pen and brown ink, with blue wash on wove paper
Verso: *Study of Coustou's Horse (in Place de la Concorde)*
Graphite
10¹/₂ x 8³/₈ (26.7 x 21.3)
Collector's stamp, lower left: *HL* (Lugt 1333)

PROVENANCE: A. C. H. His de la Salle, Paris (1795-1878); Private collection, Paris; Ian Woodner Family Collection, New York; Christie's, London, sale, July 2, 1991, no. 168.

REFERENCES: p. Grunchec, *Master Drawings by Géricault*, Washington: 1985-1986, p. 46, no. 6, fig. 6c; *Dessins français: Sculptures 1800-1930* (Paris: Galerie de Bayser, 1981), no. 25, illus. (recto and verso), unpag.; *Géricault* (Paris: Grand Palais, October 10, 1991-January 6, 1992), no. 80, p. 351.

The recto drawing is derived from an ancient engraved gem, which Géricault knew from a print. The verso drawing is a study related to *Les Chevaux de Marly* of Guillaume Coustou, monuments in the Place de la Concorde in Paris since 1798.

Illustrated, p. 24.

**Jean-Léon Gérôme (French, 1824-1904)**
34. *Drawing of the Sculpture "Ancient Dancer,"* ca. 1891
Black ink on thin white wove paper, lined with mulberry paper
11 x 8¹/₄ (28 x 21)
Signed in ink, right center: *J L Gerome*

PROVENANCE: Shepherd Gallery, New York.

**Albert Gleizes (French, 1881-1953)**
35. *Market at Courbevoie*, 1908
Black chalk heightened with white on light brown wove paper
10³/₄ x 14⁵/₈ (27.3 x 37.2)
Signed and inscribed lower right: *Albert Gleizes '08 Courbevoie*

Illustrated, p. 47.

**Jean-Baptiste Greuze (French, 1725-1805)**
36. *Head of a Boy*
Red chalk
12³/₈ x 10¹/₄ (31.4 x 26)

PROVENANCE: Mrs. Escott, London; Victor Koch, London; Rowland, Browse, and Delbanco, London; Private collection; Sotheby's, New York, sale, June 12, 1982, no. 177.

Illustrated, p. 29.

37. *Seated Woman with an Open Book, Study for "The Paralytic"*
Red chalk on cream laid paper
17¹/₈ x 12 (43.5 x 30.5)

PROVENANCE: H. Shickman Gallery, New York; Christian Humann, New York; Sotheby's, New York, sale, June 12, 1982, no. 81.

EXHIBITED: *Georgia Collects* (1989).

REFERENCES: *Georgia Collects* (1989), p. 26 illus., and p. 201.

This drawing is a study for the painting *The Paralytic*, 1760 (Hermitage Museum, St. Petersburg).

Illustrated, p. 23.

**George Grosz (American, born in Germany, 1893-1953)**
38. *Subway or Bus Scene*
Ink and graphite
23³/₄ x 17¹/₂ (60.3 x 44.5)
Signed and inscribed, lower left: *No. 19 Elek _____ fe*

PROVENANCE: Rosenfeld Fine Arts, New York; Ernest Abernathy, Atlanta.

EXHIBITED: *Drawings* (1981), no. 118; *Pathos and Passion*, High Museum at Georgia-Pacific Center, Atlanta, May 9-August 16, 1991.

REFERENCES: *Drawings*, (1981) no. 118, p. 212.

39. *Berlin Street Scene*, 1928
Pen and black and blue inks
20⅞ x 14 sight (53 x 35.6)
Signed in graphite, lower right:
*Grosz, Berlin, 1928*
Inscribed in graphite, lower left:
*No 5. [illegible]*

PROVENANCE: Rosenfeld Fine Arts, New York.

Illustrated, p. 49.

**Ernest-Hyacinthe-Constantin Guys (Dutch-French, 1802/05-1892)**
40. *Dames de la Halle*
Graphite, sepia ink heightened with yellow watercolor, and gray wash on paper, affixed to a mount
8 x 5¾ (20.2 x 14.6)
Inscribed, upper left: *Dames de la Halle / rich lace cap ribbons . . . bright silk / shall [sic] opened in front / and / behind*
Inscribed, upper right: *2299*
Inscribed, lower right: *white embroidered / apron lined with lace / . . . . scissors*

PROVENANCE: Kraushaar Galleries, New York; Mr. and Mrs. Lester Avnet, New York; Sotheby Parke Bernet, New York, sale, April 10, 1980, no. 3.

EXHIBITED: *Drawings* (1981), no. 119.

REFERENCES: *Drawings* (1981), no. 119, p. 212.

Illustrated, p. 32.

**Henri Harpignies (French, 1819-1916)**
41. *Barbizon*
Graphite
11⅛ x 8¾ (28.3 x 22.2)
Estate stamp, *Vente R. Verdun*

PROVENANCE: Raymond Verdun, Paris.

**Jean Jacques Henner (French, 1829?-1905)**
42. *Saint Sebastian tended by Saint Irene*
Black and white chalk on off-white laid paper
11⅛ x 8¾ (28.3 x 22.2)

PROVENANCE: David and Constance Yates, New York.

Henner did several paintings and drawings on this subject, including an oil painting which was shown at the Salon of 1888 and at the Exposition Universelle of 1889. The painting is now in the Musée Henner, Paris, and the large finished drawing has been in the collection of the Los Angeles County Museum of Art since 1991.

Illustrated, p. 34.

**Adolph Hirémy Hirschl (Hungarian, 1860-1933)**
43. *Violinist*
Charcoal on blue paper
11½ x 8 (29.2 x 20.3)

PROVENANCE: William Gwynn.

**Henri-Gabriel Ibels (French, 1867-1936)**
44. *Portrait of Madame Jeanne Bloch*, ca. 1892-1898
Pastel
11 x 9 (27.9 x 22.9)
Signed, lower left: *H. G. Ibels*

PROVENANCE: Paul Prouté, Paris.

Illustrated, p. 36.

**Jean-Auguste-Dominique Ingres (French, 1780-1867)**
45. *Study of Cloaks*
Graphite on laid paper
4½ x 4¾ (11.4 x 12)
Slightly irregular lower edge
Artist's estate stamp (Lugt 1477), lower right.

PROVENANCE: Petit, Paris, sale, April 27 and May 6-7, 1867; Christie's, New York, sale, October 29, 1986. no. 296.

Illustrated, p. 29.

**Louis Legrande (French, 1863-1951)**
46. *Gare Batagnolles*, ca. 1890
Ink and collage
13 x 9 (33 x 22.9)
Signed, lower right: *LeGrande*

PROVENANCE: Caspari Collection; Karl and Faber, Munich.

**Henri Lehmann (French, 1814-1882)**
47. Recto: *Studies of a Young Boy, Standing Nude*, 1859
Verso: *Studies of a Young Boy*
Graphite
11¾ x 8⅝ (29. 8 x 21.9)
Inscribed, lower center: *21 May 59*
Artist's estate stamp on the mount, lower right.

PROVENANCE: Bruno de Bayser, Paris.

EXHIBITED: *Henri Lehmann 1814-1882, Dessins*, Galerie de Bayser, Paris, June 17-July 2, 1983, no. 45.

REFERENCES: *Henri Lehmann 1814-1882, Dessins* (Paris: Galerie de Bayser, 1983), no. 45, p. 11 illus.; M. M. Aubrun, *Henri Lehmann, Catalogue Raisonné de l'Oeuvre* (Paris, 1984), Vol. I, D. 893, p. 215; Vol. II, D. 893, p. 201, illus.

These studies are preparatory for the figure of an angel in Lehmann's painting *Adveniat regnum tuum* (Thy kingdom come), part of the artist's large decorative program illustrating the Lord's Prayer for the upper register of the church of Sainte-Clotilde in Paris. The program was never carried out.

Illustrated, p. 33.

**Léon Augustin Lhermitte (French, 1844-1925)**
48. *Portrait of an Old Woman*
Charcoal on paper squared in white
23½ x 17 (59.7 x 43)

PROVENANCE: Charles A. Jackson, Manchester, 1937; Sotheby's, London, sale, November 27, 1991, no. 212.

Illustrated, p. 34.

**Maximilien Luce (French, 1858-1941)**
49. *Studies of Hands and Feet*, 1894
Ink and brush and ink wash on tan paper
8⅝ x 10¾ sight (21.9 x 27.3)
Signed and dated, lower right: *Luce Mazas 9.94*

PROVENANCE: Paul Vallotton, S. A., Lausanne; Galerie Koller, Zurich, auction 50/2, June 34, 1983, no 5475.

**Aristide Maillol (French, 1861-1944)**
50. *Seated Woman*
Red chalk heightened with white chalk on tan paper
14½ x 10½ (37 x 26.5)
Initialed, lower left: *M*

PROVENANCE: Christie's East, New York, sale, May 31, 1984, no. 12.

Illustrated, p. 45.

**Edouard Manet (French, 1832-1883)**
51. *Portrait of Henri Vignaux*, 1874
Graphite on paper mounted on board
5 x 3¾ (12.5 x 9)
Signed, lower left: *Manet, à lui ami Vigneux [sic]*

PROVENANCE: Auguste Pellerin, Paris; Vente Anonyme [Pellerin], May 7, 1926, no. 61; Christie's, New York, sale, May 14, 1980, no. 6.

EXHIBITED: *Drawings* (1981), no. 12; *Georgia Collects* (1989).

REFERENCES: E. Bazire, *Manet* (Paris: 1884), p. 31; Denis Rouart and Daniel Wildenstein, *Edouard Manet: catalogue raisonné* (Lausanne-Paris: 1975), Vol. II, no. 471, p. 170; *Drawings* (1981), no. 12, pp. 30-31; *Georgia Collects* (1989), p. 58 illus.

Illustrated, p. 35.

**Henri Martin (French, 1860-1943)**
52. *Portrait of Alexandre Charpentier*
Charcoal on tan paper
27-38 x 15¾ (69.5 x 40.2)
Signed, lower right: *Henri Martin*

PROVENANCE: Sotheby's, London, May 18, 1988, no. 21.

EXHIBITED: *Exposition des Amis des Arts*, Bordeaux, 1907, no. 418.

This drawing is a study for the painting *Inspiration* (Musée de Picardie, Amiens).

**Jean-Louis-Ernest Meissonier (French, 1815-1891)**
53. *Studies for the "Livre du Mariage,"* 1840
Graphite and brown ink
8½ x 8¼ (21.6 x 21)

Initialed, lower right: *EM*

PROVENANCE: Shepherd Gallery, New York; Christie's, New York, sale, October 26, 1988, no. 291.

EXHIBITED: *The Exhibition of the Works of Meissonier,* Paris, Georges Petit's Gallery, 1893, no. 524.

REFERENCES: *Catalogue des Tableaux, Études, Peintes, Aquarelles et Dessins composant l'Atelier Meissonier* (Paris: Galerie Georges Petit, 1893), no. 524, p. 122; *The Exhibition of the Works of Meissonier* (Paris: Georges Petit's Gallery, 1893), no. 524, p. 115.

Illustrated, p. 32.

**Adolf von Menzel (German, 1815-1905)**
54. *Study of a Man's Head,* 1903
Graphite
8¾ x 5¾ (22.5 x 14.5)
Signed with monogram and dated, lower left: *Nov. 1903*

PROVENANCE: Carlos G. Liebmann, Berlin; Sotheby's, Munich, June 25, 1992, no. 7.

Illustrated, p. 42.

**Constantin Emile Meunier (Belgian, 1831-1905)**
55. *Portrait of a Miner,* 1887
Black chalk with stumping on off-white wove paper
21⅝ x 19¼ (54.9 x 48.9)
Signed, lower right: *C Meunier*
Inscribed, lower edge: *Le Docteur Gerard Barthelemy le heros du puits de la Boule du Rieu de Coeur. Offert à Monsieur Le Docteur Barthelemy par le personnel du dispensaire Sainte Barbe à Quaregnan en temoignage de son admiration et de sa gratitude pour courage lors de la catastroph du 4 mars 1887*

PROVENANCE: Dr. Gerard Barthelemy; Patrick Derom, Brussels.

This drawing was a gift from miners to Gerard Barthelemy, a doctor who had saved many of them in a mine disaster at La Boule du Rieu de Couer on March 4, 1887.

Illustrated, p. 39.

**Amedeo Modigliani (Italian, 1884-1920)**
56. *Figure in a Turban (Portrait of Nijinski?),* 1915-1916
Blue graphite laid down on paper, mounted on board
15¾ x 10½ (40 x 27.7)
Signed, lower right: *Modigliani*

PROVENANCE: C. W. Kraushaar Art Galleries, New York; J. J. Klejman Gallery,

New York; Ralph M. Coe Collection (to 1959); Dr. and Mrs. Robert Schermer, Shaker Heights, Ohio; Dayton Art Institute, Dayton, Ohio; Sotheby Park Bernet, New York, sale, May 27, 1976, no. 221.

EXHIBITED: *Drawings* (1981), no. 48.

REFERENCES: *Drawings* (1981), no. 48, pp. 100-101.

Illustrated, p. 45.

**Roderick O'Conor (Irish, 1860-1940)**
57. *The Sea,* 1893
Ink and wash
12 x 8¼ (30.5 x 21)
Signed and dated, lower right: *R. O'Conor 93*

**Jules Pascin (American, born in Bulgaria, 1885-1930)**
58. *Café Scene,* Paris, 1921
Watercolor and ink
13 x 8½ (33 x 21.6)
Signed, lower right: *Pascin*

PROVENANCE: Wood Gaylor; Rosenfeld Fine Arts, New York.

REFERENCES: Yves Hemin, Guy Krohg, Klaus Perls, Abel Rambert, *Pascin: Catalogue raisonné* (Paris: 1991), Vol IV, no. 700, p. 389, and p. 222 illus.

Illustrated, p. 47.

**Pablo Picasso (Spanish, 1881-1973)**
59. *Study for "The Kiss"*
Graphite
13 x 19⅞ (33 x 42.2)
Signed and dated, upper right: 8.10.67. II Picasso

PROVENANCE: Private collection, New York.

REFERENCES: Charles Feld, *Picasso: His Recent Drawings, 1966-1968* (New York: Harry N. Abrams, 1969), no. 309, illus.; Christian Zervos, *Pablo Picasso, Vol. 27: Oeuvres de 1967 et 1968* (Paris: Editions "Cahiers d'art," 1973), no. 135, pl. 40.

Illustrated, p. 50.

60. *Bust of a Man,* 1943
Graphite on thin-lined paper
14 x 9¼ (35.6 x 23.5)
Dated in graphite, lower right: *24.10.43.*

PROVENANCE: Marie-Thérèse Walter; Maya Picasso.

EXHIBITED: *Georgia Collects* (1989).

REFERENCES: Christian Zervos, *Pablo Picasso, Vol. 13: Oeuvres de 1943 et 1944* (Paris: Editions "Cahiers d'art," 1962), no. 160, pl. 84; *Georgia Collects* (1989), p. 155 illus.

Illustrated, p. 50.

61. *Jean Who Laughs, Jean Who Cries,* recto and verso
Ink and watercolor on cardboard
17 x 13¼ sight (43.2 x 33.6)

PROVENANCE: Marie-Thérèse Walter;

Maya Picasso.

EXHIBITED: *Un Collection Picasso, Oeuvres de 1937 à 1946* [Collection of works belonging to Marie-Thérèse Walter], Galerie Jan Krugier, Geneva, 1973, no. 126.

REFERENCES: Florens Deuchler, *Un Collection Picasso, Oeuvres de 1937 à 1946* (Geneva: Galerie Jan Krugier, 1973), no. 126, illus.; Josep Palau i Fabre, *Pare Picasso* (Barcelona: Ediciones Poligrafa, n. d.), no. 16, p. 18 illus.

**Isidore Alexandre Auguste Pils (French 1813-1875)**
62. Sketch Book, 39 pages
Graphite, crayon, and watercolor
11¼ x 8½ (28.6 x 21.6)
Signed and dated on numerous pages.

63. *Study of Hands and a Skull*
Charcoal, red and white chalk
15 x 10¾ (38 x 27.3)
Inscription at lower center edge is illegible.

PROVENANCE: Private collection, New York; Eric Carlson, New York; Christie's East, New York, sale, November 25, 1987, no. 183.

**Camille Pissarro (French, 1831-1903)**
64. *Child at Table (Ludovic-Rodolphe?),* ca. 1880
Graphite
12⅜ x 7¾ (31.4 x 19.7)
Stamp (Lugt 613a) signed, lower right, with initials: *CP*

PROVENANCE: Folio Fine Art, London; Sotheby Parke Bernet, New York, sale, November 8, 1979, no. 703.

EXHIBITED: *Drawings* (1981), no. 19.

REFERENCES: *Drawings* (1981), no. 19, pp. 44-45, illus.

This drawing is a preliminary sketch for the gouache of 1880 entitled *Enfants à table* (see L.-R. Pissarro and L. Venturi, *Camille Pissarro, son art, son oeuvre,* vol. II, pl. 261, no. 1334). The chair with the curved back seen here also appears in other Pissarro family interiors. See John Rewald, *Camille Pissarro* (New York, 1963), pp. 129 and 133.)

Illustrated, p. 37.

65. *The Family of the Artist,* ca. 1895
Pen and sepia ink
8¾ x 7 (22 x 18)
Initialed, lower left, in sepia ink: *CP*
Inscribed, lower right: *La famille . . . [illegible]*

PROVENANCE: Collection of Mr. Michael M. Zagayski; Anonymous sale, Parke-Bernet Galleries, New York, December 13, 1967, no. 11; Mrs. Lester R. Bachner; Christie's, New York, sale, February 14, 1991, no. 22.

EXHIBITED: *Camille Pissarro 1830-1903: A Memorial Exhibit*, The Jewish Museum, New York, 1953.

REFERENCES: *Camille Pissarro 1830-1903: A Memorial Exhibit* (New York: The Jewish Museum, 1953), illus. (cover); Ralph E. Shikes and Paula Harper, *Pissarro: His Life and Work* (New York: Horizon Press, 1980), pp. 279-281, illus.

Pissarro's family is shown as follows: Paul Emile and Cocotte are painting at easels, and Lucien is instructing them. Georges is working at an etching table. Felix and Rodo have portfolios of drawings under their arms. Julie is pictured sewing.

Illustrated, p. 37.

**Armand Point (French, 1860-1932)**
66. *Portrait of Madame Berthelot,* 1895
Charcoal and colored chalks
17 x 12¼ (43 x 31)
Signed and dated, lower left:
*A Point 1895*

PROVENANCE: Mme. Philippe Berthelot; Mme. A. Langlois-Berthelot, Paris; Sotheby's, London, sale, June 16, 1993, no. 284.

EXHIBITED: *French Symbolist Painters,* Hayward Gallery, London, June 7-July 23, and Walker Art Gallery, Liverpool, August 9-September, 1972, no. 196.

REFERENCES: *French Symbolist Painters* (London: Hayward Gallery, 1972), no. 196, p. 98 illus.

Illustrated, p. 25.

**Jean-François Raffaëlli (French, 1850-1924)**
67. *À l'Hôtel des Ventes, Salle Drouot, Paris (Broker in the Mazas, Hôtel Drouot),* ca. 1888
India ink and watercolor on paper laid down on board
9⅛ x 10 (23 x 25.4)
Signed, lower right: *JF Raffaelli*

PROVENANCE: L. Megret; Leicester Galleries, London; Benjamin Sonnenberg; Mrs. Benjamin Sonnenberg; Sotheby's, New York, sale, November 21, 1980, no. 143; Private collection, New York; Sotheby's, New York, sale, May 22, 1991, no. 179.

EXHIBITED: *List of Loans at the Opening Exhibition of the Modern Foreign Gallery,* National Gallery, London, 1926.

REFERENCES: Theodore Child, "The Hotel Drouot," *Harper's New Monthly Magazine,* Vol. LXXVIII, no. 165, February 1889, pp. 331-347, illus., p. 346; *List of Loans at the Opening Exhibition of the Modern Foreign Gallery* (London: National Gallery, 1926), p. 9.

Illustrated, p. 40.

**Denis-August-Marie Raffet (French, 1804-1860)**
68. *A French Soldier,* 1857
Pen and brown ink
6 x 4¾ (15.2 x 12.1)
Signed, lower left: *Raffet*
Inscription, lower left: *à mon /son?/ ami Eugene 28 aout 1857*

PROVENANCE: Robert Prouté, Paris, June 1957; E. Maurice Bloch Collection; Christie's, New York, sale, June 19, 1990, no. 138.

**Paul Ranson (French, 1864-1909)**
69. *Brittany Landscape,* ca. 1892
Colored crayons, charcoal, and colored graphites on laid paper
12 x 18⅛ (30.5 x 46.4)
Stamp signed, lower right.

PROVENANCE: Bator Collection; Sotheby Parke Bernet, New York, sale, October 18, 1979, no. 12a.

EXHIBITED: *The Nabis,* Pennsylvania State University College of Arts and Architecture, College Park, Pa., February 1-28, 1971, no. 19; *Drawings* (1981), no. 134.

REFERENCES: *The Nabis* (College Park, Pa.: Pennsylvania State University College of Arts and Architecture, 1971), no. 19, illus.; *Drawings* (1981), no. 134, p. 213 (listed as *Mountain Landscape*).

Illustrated, p. 43.

**Pierre Auguste Renoir (French, 1841-1919)**
70. *Drawing after Manet's "Fifer,"* 1883
Crayon
17½ x 10¾ (44.5 x 27.3)
Inscribed, lower right: *Renoir d'apres Manet*

PROVENANCE: Mrs. Chester Dale; Wildenstein & Co., New York; William Doyle, New York.

EXHIBITED: *Drawings from the Drawing Society's Membership,* Hirschl and Adler Galleries, New York, February 12-March 8, 1986; *Georgia Collects* (1989).

REFERENCES: John Rewald, ed., *Renoir Drawings* (New York: 1946), no. 17, p. 19, illus.; John Rewald, *Studies in Impressionism* (New York: 1985), no. 9, p. 23, illus.; François Daulte, letter, January 4, 1985, with opinion of authenticity; Daniel M. Mendelowitz and Duane A. Wakeham, *A Guide to Drawing* (New York: Harcourt Brace Jovanovich, 1993, fifth edition), p. 53, illus.

This drawing was made at the time of a memorial exhibition of Manet's work held soon after the artist's death, and it was published in *La Vie Moderne* (January 12, 1884). See Rewald, *Studies in Impressionism,* p. 23.

Illustrated, p. 35.

**Théodule Augustin Ribot (French, 1823-1891)**
71. *Portrait of the Artist's Daughter*
Watercolor and black ink on off-white wove paper
7½ x 5⅛₆ (19 x 12.8)
Signed, upper left: *T. Ribot*

PROVENANCE: A. Marmontel, Paris.

Illustrated, p. 38.

**August Rodin (French, 1840-1917)**
72. *Woman*
Watercolor and graphite
13 x 10 (33 x 25.4)
Signed, lower right: *A Rodin*

Illustrated, p. 27.

**Georges Rouault (French, 1871-1958)**
73. *To a Creole Woman*
Black touche
4¾ x 3⅜ (12 x 8)

PROVENANCE: Hammer Galleries, New York; Bill Haddaway, Texas.

REFERENCES: Bernard Dorival, with catalogue by Isabelle Rouault, *Rouault: L'Oeuvre Peint* (Monte-Carlo, 1988), no. 1165, p. 330 illus.

This sketch was one commissioned by Ambroise Vollard about 1926 for a portfolio of lithographs illustrating Baudelaire's *Les Fleurs du Mal.* The lithographs were never published.

Illustrated, p. 46.

**Ker Xavier Roussel (French, 1867-1944)**
74. *Portrait of Vuillard*
Graphite
5¾ x 4 (14.6 x 10)

PROVENANCE: Paul Prouté, Paris; Galerie Coligny, Paris.

**Theo Van Rysselberghe (Belgian, 1862-1926)**
75. *Mother and Child*
Pastel and charcoal on buff paper
21 x 16 (53.3 x 40.6)
Monogram, lower right

PROVENANCE: Alexander Kahan Fine Arts, New York.

Illustrated, p. 25.

**Claude Emile Schuffenecker (French, 1851-1934)**
76. *Portrait of Emile Bernard*
Charcoal
9 x 7½ (22.9 x 19)
Estate stamp, lower right.

PROVENANCE: Joan and Lester Avnet, New York.

**Paul Sérusier (French, 1863-1927)**
77. *Sketches of Gauguin and Ranson,* 1888-1890
Charcoal and ink on tan paper
12 x 18⅞ (30.5 47.9)
Stamped with initials, lower left.

PROVENANCE: Marguerite Sérusier; Collection Mlle. H. Boutaric, Paris;

Ader Picard Tajan, Paris, sale, June 20, 1984, no. 392.

REFERENCES: Henri Perruchot, *Gauguin* (New York?: Ward Publishing, 1974), no. 24 illus.; John Rewald, *Post-Impressionism from Van Gogh to Gauguin* (New York: The Museum of Modern Art, 1978, third edition), p. 255 illus.; Marcel Guichteau with Georgette Guicheteau, *Paul Sérusier* (Pontoise: 1989), vol. 2. no. 23, p. 87 illus., p. 89; Daniel Wildenstein and Raymond Cogniat, *Gauguin* (Garden City, N. Y.: 1974), p. 37.

Illustrated, p. 44.

78. *Studies of Breton Peasant Women*, ca. 1892
Watercolor, brown wash heightened with white on paper mounted on board
10³/₄ x 9¹/₂ (27.3 x 24.1)
Inscribed in graphite, lower right edge: *Pont-Aven*
Estate stamp, lower right.

PROVENANCE: Christie's, New York, sale, November 1, 1978, no. 95.

EXHIBITED: *Drawings* (1981), no. 27.

REFERENCES: Marcel Guichteau, *Paul Sérusier* (Paris: 1976), no. 92, p. 216; *Drawings* (1981), no. 27, pp. 60-61 illus.

Illustrated, p. 44.

**Georges Seurat (French, 1859-1891)**
79. *Ulysses and the Suitors*, 1876
Graphite
9¹/₈ x 12¹/₂ (23.2 x 31.7)
Signed and dated, lower right: *28 Novembre 1876 Seurat*
Illegible inscription, lower edge.
Monogram of Félix Fénéon, lower right.

PROVENANCE: Félix Fénéon, Paris; sale, Hôtel Drouot, Paris, April 30, 1947, Lot 60]; Mr. and Mrs. William Goetze, Hillsborough, California; Christie's, New York, sale, Ocotber 8, 1992, no. 2.

EXHIBITED: *Les Dessins de Georges Seurat*, Galerie Bernheim-Jeune, Paris, November-December 1926, no. 10; *Seurat and his Friends*, Hammer Galleries, New York, October 30-November 17, 1962, no. 7; *Modern Graphics from San Diego Collectors*, La Jolla Art Center, La Jolla, California, January 10-February 17, 1963.

REFERENCES: Gustave Kahn, *Les Dessins de Georges Seurat* (Paris: Bernheim-Jeune, 1928), pl. 10 illus.; C. M. de Hauke and Paul Brame, *Seurat et Son Oeuvre* (Paris: 1961), vol. II, no. 233, p. 7, illus.; J. Russell, *Seurat* (London: Thames & Hudson, 1965), p. 12, fig. 3, illus.; Erich Franz and Bernd Growe, *Georges Seurat Drawings* (Boston: New York Graphic Society, 1984), p. 52, fig. 2 illus.; R. Thomson, *Seurat* (Oxford: 1985) no. 10, p. 52 illus.; M. Zimmermann, *Seurat* (Antwerp: 1991), p. 27.

Illustrated, p. 41.

80. *Portrait of a Man, After Holbein*
Graphite
11¹/₄ x 7¹/₄ (28.6 x 18.4)

PROVENANCE: Mme. Camille Platteel; Félix Fénéon; Paul Eluard.

EXHIBITED: *D'après les Maîtres*, Galerie Bernheim-Jeune, Paris, April 18-20, 1910, no. 48; *Les Dessins de Georges Seurat*, Galerie Bernheim-Jeune, Paris, November 28-December 24, 1926, no. 12; *Kunstlerkopien*, Kunsthalle, Basel, September 18-October 17, 1937, no. 57.

REFERENCES: *D'après les Maîtres* (Paris: Galerie Bernheim-Jeune, 1910), no. 48; *Les Dessins de Georges Seurat* (Paris: Galerie Bernheim-Jeune, 1926), no. 12; Gustave Kahn, *Les dessins de Georges Seurat* (Paris: Bernheim-Jeune, 1928), pl. 12 illus.

81. *Study of Soldiers*, 1880
Graphite and colored crayons
5⁷/₈ x 9¹/₄ (14.9 x 23.5)
Inscription in blue on the back of the original mount: *Dessin de Seurat/15 cm x 24 cm* and initialed *p. S.* and *ff* and with the dedication *À Madame Laurent Delkire (?), ces guerriers dessinés par Seurat en 1879-80 à Brest, ou il faisait son volontariat d'un an. Félix Fénéon.*

PROVENANCE: Emile Seurat; Félix Fénéon; Madame Delkire (?); Sale Gutekunst and Klipstein, Berne, June 5-6, 1959, no. 779; M. Knoedler and Co., New York; Sotheby Parke Bernet, New York, sale, November 8, 1979, no. 715.

EXHIBITED: *Georges Seurat*, Galerie Paul Rosenberg, Paris, February 3-29, 1936, no. 58; *Drawings* (1981), no. 21; *Georgia Collects* (1989).

REFERENCES: C. M. de Hauke, *Seurat et son oeuvre* (Paris: 1961), vol. II, no. 364, p. 44, and p. 45 illus.; *Drawings* (1981) no. 21, pp. 48-49, illus.; *Georgia Collects* (1989), p. 58, illus.

This drawing is from a notebook Seurat kept during his year's military service, which began in November 1879, and in which he recorded the activities of his fellow soldiers.

Illustrated, p. 27.

82. *Fleuron de laurier*, ca. 1875
Black chalk
18⁷/₈ x 12³/₄ (47.9 x 32.3)

PROVENANCE: Félix Fénéon, Paris (collector's sale stamp on the reverse [Lugt 924a]); sale, Hôtel Drouot, Paris, July 9, 1947, lot 90; Anonymous sale, Christie's, London, June 25, 1985, no. 328; Ian Woodner, and by descent to Dian Woodner and Andrea Woodner; Christie's, New York, sale, May 13, 1993, no. 115.

**Alfred Sisley (French, 1839-1899)**
83. *Landscape*, 1888
Charcoal on gray paper
6 x 7³/₈ (15 x 18.8)
Signed and dated, lower left: *Sisley 88*

PROVENANCE: Sotheby's, London, sale, May 20, 1987, no. 73.

According to François Daulte, this drawing is probably a study for one of the paintings entitled *La Route de Veneux à Moret*, which Sisley painted ca. 1887-1890. (Private communication, Sotheby's, London, May 20, 1987.)

Illustrated, p. 37.

**François Clement Sommier, called Henri Somm (French, 1844-1907)**
84. *Oriental Scene and Woman with a Fan*
Watercolor and graphite on fan-shaped paper
18¹/₄ x 6¹/₂ (46.4 x 16.5)
Signed, lower right: *Henri Somm*

PROVENANCE: Douwes Fine Arts, London.

**Théophile Steinlen (French, born in Switzerland, 1859-1923)**
85. *Illustration for "Gil Blas"*
Colored crayons
16¹/₄ x 15¹/₄ (41.3 x 38.7)
Signed, lower right: *Steinlen*

Illustrated, p. 40.

**Pavel Tchelitchew (American, born in Russia, 1898-1957)**
86. *Mad Woman*, 1937
Silverpoint
19¹/₄ x 12¹/₂ (49 x 31.5)
Signed and dated, lower right: *P. Tchelitchew 37*

PROVENANCE: Arthur Tooth, London; Edward F. W. James; Christie's, New York, sale, October 6, 1988, no. 94.

EXHIBITED: *Phenomena*, Arthur Tooth & Sons, London, June-July 1938, no. 16; *The Fine Line: Drawing with Silver*, Norton Gallery and School of Art, West Palm Beach, Florida, March 23-May 5, 1985, no. 72.

REFERENCES: *Phenomena* (London: Arthur Tooth & Sons, 1938), no. 16; Bruce Weber, *The Fine Line: Drawing with Silver* (West Palm Beach, Florida: Norton Gallery and School of Art, 1985), no. 72, p. 85 illus., and p. 101.

Illustrated, p. 46.

**Jacques-Joseph Tissot (French, 1836-1902)**
87. *Preparatory Study for "The Departure of the Prodigal Son from Venice,"* ca. 1862
Graphite heightened with white body color on grey paper
9¹/₄ x 9⁷/₈ (23.5 x 25.1)

PROVENANCE: David Daniels, New York; Sotheby's, New York, sale, October 13, 1993, no. 30.

EXHIBITED: *French Artists in Italy, 17th to 19th Century*, Dayton Art Institute, Dayton, Ohio, October 15-November 18, 1971, no. 54; *Christian Imagery in French 19th Century Art, 1789-1906*, Shepherd Gallery, New York, Spring 1980.

REFERENCES: *French Artists in Italy, 17th to 19th Century* (Dayton, Ohio: Dayton Art Institute, 1971), no. 54; *Christian Imagery in French 19th Century Art, 1789-1906* (New York: Shepherd Gallery, Spring 1980), no. 137, p. 351 illus.; Michael Wentworth, *James Tissot* (Oxford: 1984), p. 40, pl. 17 illus.

This drawing was made in preparation for the painting *The Departure of the Prodigal Son from Venice*, ca. 1862, which was exhibited at the Paris Salon of 1863. Two other preparatory studies are in the collection of the Metropolitan Museum of Art, New York.

Illustrated, p. 33.

## Henri de Toulouse-Lautrec (French, 1864-1901)

88. *Mademoiselle Lender*[?], ca. 1895
    Pen and ink
    8 x 6½ (20.3 x 16.5)
    Collector's stamp of Mme. Thadée (Misia) Natanson, lower right, verso: *T.N.-H. T-L*

PROVENANCE: Mme. Thadée Natanson, Paris; Sale Hôtel Drouot, Paris, Nov. 27, 1953, Lot 129; M. Gobin, Paris; Private collection; Huguette Berès, Paris; Christie's, New York, sale, November 5, 1982, no. 309.

REFERENCES: T. Natanson, *Un Henri de T.-Lautrec* (Geneva: 1952), pp. 180 and 219 illus.; M. G. Dortu, *Toulouse-Lautrec et son Oeuvre* (New York: 1971), vol. VI, no. D.3.970, p. 676 illus.

Illustrated, p. 36.

## Louis Valtat (French, 1869-1952)

89. *Woman near a Lake*, ca. 1896-98
    Watercolor and graphite
    9 ³/₈ x 12¼ (23.8 x 31.1)
    Initialed, lower right.

PROVENANCE: David Hughes, London; Christie's, New York, sale, October 22, 1980, no. 319.

EXHIBITED: *Drawings* (1981), no. 142.

REFERENCES: *Drawings* (1981), no. 142, p. 213.

## Jehan Georges Vibert (French, 1840-1902)

90. *The Knife Grinder*
    Pen and ink
    6 ⁵/₈ x 4 ½ sight (16.8 x 11.4)
    Signed, lower left: *J. G. Vibert*

PROVENANCE: Private Collection, New York.

Illustrated, p. 38.

## Edouard Vuillard (French, 1868-1940)

91. *Madame Vuillard*
    Graphite
    8⅛ x 4½ (20.5 x 11.5)
    Stamped (Lugt 909c) with initials, lower right.

PROVENANCE: Jean-Claude Bellier, Paris; Christie's, New York, sale, November 5, 1981, no. 307.

## Benjamin West (American, 1738-1820)

92. *Lion*
    Black and white chalk on blue paper
    6³/₈ x 10 (16.2 x 25.4)

PROVENANCE: E. Maurice Bloch; Christie's, New York, sale, January 9, 1991, no. 44.

This drawing is probably a preparatory study for the recumbent lion in *Omnia Vincit Amor*, 1809 (Metropolitan Museum of Art, New York).

Illustrated, p. 23.

## Adolphe Léon Willette (French, 1857-1926)

93. *La République eclairant le monde . . . des fonctionnaires*
    Graphite, ink, and colored chalks
    14³/₄ x 20½ (37.5 x 52)
    Signed, lower right: *A. Willette*
    Inscriptions in black ink, above figures, left to right: *AUGUSTE POTACOLLEE / Le crachoir de l'Elysée / 50,000 fs. . . . . ./ 250,000 fs. avec les pourboires·*// *JOSEPH PRUDHOMME / President de la R.F. / 1200000 fs.* // *Le BOURREAU 6,000 fs. / avec les deplacements et les gratifications / 30,000 fs.;* below figures, left to right: *La République eclairant le monde . . . des fonctionnaires* Inscribed in blue chalk, upper right: *mille francs*

PROVENANCE: J. Chavasse; Arsene Bonafous-Murat, Paris.

Illustrated, p. 41.

## SCULPTURE

## Emile-Antoine Bourdelle (French, 1861-1929)

94. *Head of a Warrior*, ca. 1894-1900
    Bronze, with green patina
    Height: 18¼ (46.4)
    Monogram, lower right.
    Inscribed, on reverse, lower right, on bronze base: *C by Bourdelle / Suisse Fondeur, Paris No. 1*

PROVENANCE: Arezzo Fine Arts Inc., New York; Christie's East, New York, sale, November 13, 1990, no. 17.

This sculpture is a study for the *Monument aux Morts, aux Combattants et aux Serviteurs du Tarn-et-Garonne*, erected in 1902 in Montauban, Bourdelle's home town. This study was first cast in 1966 under the supervision of Mme. Bourdelle and her daughter Rhodia Dufet Bourdelle.

Illustrated, p. 59.

## Jean-Baptiste Carpeaux (French, 1827-1875)

95. *Eugène Giraud*
    Plaster
    Height: 26 (66)
    Inscribed, on right [shoulder]: *Carpeaux*

PROVENANCE: David and Constance Yates, New York.

Illustrated, p. 57.

96. *Victor Thiébaut*
    Bronze
    Height: 7¼ (18.4)
    Inscribed, on right [shoulder]: *B. Carpeaux*

PROVENANCE: André Lemaire, Paris.

EXHIBITED: *A Romance with Realism: The Art of Jean-Baptiste Carpeaux*, Sterling and Francine Clark Art Institute, Williamstown, Mass., 1989.

REFERENCE: Jennifer Gordon Lovett, *A Romance with Realism: The Art of Jean-Baptiste Carpeaux* (Williamstown, Mass.: Sterling and Francine Clark Art Institute, 1989), p. 48.

Illustrated, p. 56.

## Alexandre-Louis-Marie Charpentier (French, 1856-1909)

97. *Mother and Child*, ca. 1883
    Bronze
    17³/₄ x 11⁷/₈ x 1 (45 x 30.2)
    Inscribed, lower right: *Alexandre Charpentier*

PROVENANCE: Patrice Barbé, Paris.

98. *Mother and Child*, 1892
    Plaster
    16³/₄ x 11¼ sight (45.5 x 28.6)
    Inscribed, lower right: *Alexandre Charpentier 1892*

PROVENANCE: David and Constance Yates, New York.

Illustrated, p. 58.

99. *Portrait of C. E. Meunier*, 1899
Bronze
7³/₈ x 6¹/₂ x ³/₄ (18.7 x 16.5 x 1.9)
Inscribed, upper right: *Constantin Meunier 28 Fevrier 1899*
Monogram, center left.

PROVENANCE: Canale Collection, Paris.

100. *Chess*
Bronze patiné
3¹/₄ x 6¹/₁₆ (8.3 x 15.4)
Initialed, upper left.

101. *Dominoes*
Bronze patiné
3¹/₈ x 5¹⁵/₁₆ (7.9 x 15)
Initialed, upper right.

PROVENANCE: David and Constance Yates, New York.

**Auguste Clésinger (French, 1814-1883)**
102. *Tragedy*
Bronze
12 x 6¹/₄ x 5³/₄ (30.5 x 15.9 x 14.6)

PROVENANCE: André Lemaire, Paris.

**Jules Dalou (French, 1838-1902)**
103. *Lafayette*
Bronze
Height: 14³/₄ (37.5)
Inscriptions, on bronze base, front: *LAFAYETTE*; left: *Susse Fes Edt*; right: *DALOU*; back: monogram; impressed with the Susse Freres foundry seal, and stamped *H* and *France*.

PROVENANCE: Christie's, New York, sale, February 25, 1987, no. 151.

This is a reduction of a model designed for a never-completed monument for Versailles commemorating the Constituent Assembly of 1789.

**David D'Angers [Pierre-Jean David] (French, 1788-1856)**
104. *Bonchamps*, 1824
Bronze
7³/₄ x 9 x 5¹/₂ (19.7 x 22.9 x 14)
Inscribed, on base, at left rear: *DAVID D'ANGERS*
Inscribed, on base: *Grace pour les prisonniers / Bonchamp le veut (?) / Froment-Meurice Ciseleur, a son ami / Wasselin des fosses, 14 Juin 1854.*

PROVENANCE: Christie's, New York, sale, May 27, 1992, no. 115.

Illustrated, p. 55.

105. *Victor Hugo*, 1828
Bronze
Diameter: 4 (10.2)
Inscribed, left and right: *Victor Hugo*
Inscribed, bottom: *David 1828*

PROVENANCE: Jacques Fischer, Paris.

106. *Géricault Pictor*, 1830
Bronze
Diameter: 5³/₄ (14.6)
Inscribed, top zone: *Gericault Pictor*
Inscribed, lower left: *David 1830*

Illustrated, p. 54.

107. *Nicolò Paganini*, 1834
Bronze
Diameter: 6¹/₈ (15.6)
Inscribed, left: *Nicolo Paganini*
Inscribed, bottom: *David 1834*

PROVENANCE: Didier Chereau, Paris.

108. *Philopomene*, 1837
Bronze
13³/₄ x 5¹/₄ x 6¹/₂ (34.9 x 13.3 x 16.5)
Foundry mark, left rear: *Thiebaut Freres, Fondeurs, Paris*

PROVENANCE: Didier Chereau, Paris.

EXHIBITED: *Georgia Collects* (1989).

REFERENCES: *Georgia Collects* (1989), p. 50, and p. 200 illus.

Illustrated, p. 55.

109. *Liberty*, 1839
Bronze
9³/₈ x 3¹/₂ x 3 (23.8 x 8.9 x 7.6)
Inscribed, on left side of base: *P. J. David/1840*
Inscribed, on front of base: *Liberté, Liberté, cherie / combats avec tex defenseurs*
Inscribed, on a triangular object on column base behind figure: *Liberté Fraternité*

PROVENANCE: Marcel Berkovitz, Brussels.

Illustrated, p. 55.

110. *Balzac*
Bronze
9³/₄ x 5¹/₂ x 4³/₄ (24.8 x 14 x 12.1)
Inscribed, on bronze base, front: *De Balzac*
Inscribed, right: *David D'Angers 1844*
Inscribed, on the reverse: *F Barbedienne Fondeur* / (foundry mark) *Reduction mecanique A. Collas Brevete*

PROVENANCE: David and Constance Yates, New York.

Illustrated, p. 54.

111. *Bérenger*
Bronze
9³/₄ x 5¹/₂ x 4³/₄ (24.8 x 14 x 12.1)
Inscribed, on base, top rear: *F. Barbedienne, Fondeur*
Inscribed, on base, bottom: (foundry mark) *Reduction mecanique A. Collas Brevete*
Inscribed, on base, right: *Offert à Bérenger par p. J. David d'Anger 1834*

PROVENANCE: David and Constance Yates, New York.

Illustrated, p. 54.

112. *Kléber*
Bronze
10⁵/₈ x 9⁷/₈ (27 x 25.1)
Inscribed, left: *Kleber*; lower right: *David 1831*

PROVENANCE: Didier Chereau, Paris.

113. *Madame Récamier*
Bronze
Diameter: 5¹/₈ (13)
Inscribed, center right: *Madame Récamier*
Inscribed, lower center edge: *David*

PROVENANCE: Arnoldi-Livie, Munich.

114. *Study for the West Facade of the Arc de Triomphe* [Marseilles]
Bronze
11¹/₄ x 10 x 10¹/₈ (28.6 x 25.4 x 25.7)

Illustrated, p. 54.

**Jules Desbois (French, 1851-1935)**
115. *Portrait of la comtesse d'Otrante*
Marble
14 x 14 x 7 (35.6 x 35.6 x 17.9)
Inscribed, lower left: *A Madame La Contesse d'Otrante*
Inscribed, lower right: *J. D.*

PROVENANCE: André Lemaire, Paris; Paris Artmarket.

**Jean-François-Marie Garnier (French, 1820-1895)**
116. *L'Enfer des Luxurieux*
Bronze, cast and embossed, brown patina
Diameter: 23 (58.4)

PROVENANCE: Audouy Collection, Paris.

Illustrated, p. 58.

**Paul Gauguin (French, 1848-1903)**
117. *Mask of a Savage*
Bronze, black patina
Height: 10 (25.4)

PROVENANCE: Walter P. Chrysler, Jr., Collection; Sotheby's, New York, sale, October 7, 1989, no. 31.

This bronze *Mask of a Savage* evolved from earlier ceramic and plaster images made by Gauguin. It resembles closely the face of the Polynesian god Fatu in Gauguin's 1893 painting *The Moon and the Earth*. The only other known bronze cast is in the Musée d'Orsay in Paris. See Marla Prather and Charles F. Stuckey, *Gauguin: A Retrospective* (New York: 1987), p. 277; and Richard Brettell, François Cachin, Claire Freches-Thory, and Charles F. Stuckey, *The Art of Paul Gauguin*, exhib. cat. (Washington, D.C.: National Gallery of Art, 1988), pp. 367-369.

Illustrated, p. 59.

**Théodore Géricault (French, 1791-1824)**
118. *L'Ecorché*
    Bronze
    5½ x 13 x 5 (14 x 33 x 12.7)

PROVENANCE: Private collection, New York.

Illustrated, p. 53.

**Jean-Françoise Legendre-Héral (French, 1796-1851)**
119. *Prometheus*, 1841
    Bronze
    13³/₈ x 9 x 9½ (34 x 22.9 x 24.1)
    Inscribed, on base, right:
    *LeGendre Heral Paris 1841*

PROVENANCE: Private collection, New York.

Illustrated, p. 53.

**Constantin Emile Meunier (Belgian, 1831-1905)**
120. *Self-Portrait*
    Bronze
    Diameter: 7⁷/₈ (20)

PROVENANCE: Marcel Berkovitz, Brussels.

**Jean-Jacques Pradier (French, 1792-1852)**
121. *Profiles of Ingres and Flandrin*, 1842
    Plaster
    9¼ x 7¼ ( 23.5 x 18.4) (oval)
    Signed, on underside of collar:
    *J. Pradier 1842*

122. *Profiles of Ingres and Flandrin*, 1842
    Bronze
    Diameter: 8⁵/₈ (21.9)
    Signed, on underside of collar:
    *J. Pradier 1842*

PROVENANCE: David and Constance Yates, New York.

123. *Sappho*
    Bronze
    11 x 14 x 6½ (27.9 x 35.6 x 16.5)
    Signed, on base: *J. Pradier*

PROVENANCE: Patrice Barbé, Paris.

Illustrated, p. 56.

**Jean-François Raffaëlli (French, 1850-1924)**
124. *Study for "Bonhomme assis sur un Banc,"* 1880s
    Bronze, black-brown patina
    10¼ x 9½ x 7 (26 x 24.1 x 17.8)

PROVENANCE: Didier Chereau, Paris.

EXHIBITED: *Georgia Collects* (1989).

REFERENCES: *Georgia Collects* (1989), p. 55 illus., and p. 201.

Illustrated, p. 59.

**Auguste Rodin (French, 1840-1917)**
125. *Polyphemus, Acis, and Galatea,* 1888
    Plaster
    11⁵/₈ x 6³/₄ x 8³/₄ (29.5 x 17.1 x 22.2)

PROVENANCE: Artist's collection; Georges DePeper, Paris, thence by descent in the DePeper family; David and Constance Yates, New York.

Rodin originally considered using the subject of Polyphemus, Acis, and Galatea in his *Gates of Hell*, the great bronze doors he was commissioned to make for the Musée des arts decoratifs in Paris. Two versions of this composition are known: the plaster version in the Rodin Museum, Philadelphia, and in the Schlossberg collection; and a bronze version, with examples in the Musée Rodin, Paris, and in the California Palace of the Legion of Honor, San Francisco. See John Tancock, *The Sculpture of Auguste Rodin* (Philadephia: Philadelphia Museum of Art, 1976), pp. 210-211, no. 22.

Illustrated, p. 60.

**Victor Joseph Jean Ambroise Segoffin (French, 1867-1925)**
126. *Philoctetes and the Sons of Asclepius,* 1897
    Terra cotta
    14½ x 11½ (36.8 x 29.2)
    Inscribed, upper right:
    *A. J. V. Segoffin 97*
    Academy stamp, upper left.

PROVENANCE: Roger Miles, Paris.

This sculpture was Segoffin's entry in the 1897 Prix de Rome competition, for which he was awarded first prize by the French Academy.

Illustrated, p. 60.